BIRDS AROUND THE WORLD

The Natural History Press, publisher for The American Museum of Natural History, is a division of Doubleday and Company, Inc. Directed by a joint editorial board made up of members of the staff of both the Museum and Doubleday, the Natural History Press publishes books and periodicals in all branches of the life and earth sciences, including anthropology and astronomy. The Natural History Press has its editorial offices at The American Museum of Natural History, Central Park West at 79th Street, New York 24, New York, and its business offices at 501 Franklin Avenue, Garden City, New York.

BIRDS AROUND THE WORLD

A GEOGRAPHICAL LOOK AT EVOLUTION AND BIRDS

Dean Amadon

CHAIRMAN OF THE DEPARTMENT OF ORNITHOLOGY AND
LAMONT CURATOR OF BIRDS
THE AMERICAN MUSEUM OF NATURAL HISTORY

Published for
The American Museum of Natural History

The Natural History Press
Garden City, New York
1966

CONTENTS

ILLUSTRATIONS   ix

Chapter 1   FIRST PRINCIPLES   1
            Evolution and Distribution   9

Chapter 2   THE EFFECT OF PHYSICAL BARRIERS   19
            Water and Land   21
            Chance   25
            Introduced Species   33

Chapter 3   ECOLOGICAL REQUIREMENTS   37
            Food and Water   39
            Shelter   43
            Migration   49
            The Ecological Niche   55

Chapter 4   HARMFUL   AND   BENEFICIAL   FAC-
            TORS   63
            Predators and Parasites   65
            Climate   67
            Man's Impact   70
            Beneficial Factors   71

Chapter 5 SPECIES DYNAMICS AND DISTRI-
BUTION   75
When Species Meet   84
Declining Species   92
Dominant Species   100

Chapter 6 DISTRIBUTION OF HIGHER SYSTEM-
ATIC CATEGORIES   105
The Crow Family   121

Chapter 7 GEOGRAPHICAL PATTERNS OF DIS-
TRIBUTION—FAUNAS   125
Barriers   130
Comparing the Regions   131
The Regions and Past Distribu-
tion   134
Lesser Faunal Units   137
Value of Faunal Analysis   141

Chapter 8 ECOLOGICAL SYSTEMS OF CLASSI-
FYING DISTRIBUTION   143
Life Zones   147
Biotic Provinces   149
Biomes   151

FURTHER READING   161

INDEX   165

ILLUSTRATIONS

Figure

1. The Dodo—a problem in distribution.   3
2. Distribution on a uniform planet.   7
3. Effect of change in climate.   10
4. Effect of change in ocean level.   11
5. Geological timetable of birds.   13
6. Family tree of birds—radiation and extinction.   14
7. Recent and fossil distribution of certain geese.   15
8. Contrasting distributions of two related pigeons.   24
9. Element of chance—the Short-eared Owl.   27
10. Dispersal in rails.   30, 31
11. Population explosion in an introduced bird.   34
12. Need for shelter in the quail.   44
13. Competition for the same nest.   46
14. Contrast of winter and summer habitat.   50
15. Migration in the tropics—the Pennant-winged Nightjar.   52

16. Ecological races—the Song Sparrow.   56
17. The ecological niche.   58
18. Habitat selection is innate.   61
19. The feather mite—a parasite.   66
20. The effect of geographical isolation.   82
21. Isolation—Savannah and Ipswich spar-
    rows.   86
22. Repulsion in closely related species.   88
23. The California Condor.   93
24. Distribution and migration of Kirtland's
    Warbler.   96
25. Factors in the extinction of the Hawai-
    ian Mamo.   99
26. Classic biogeographical regions of the
    world.   127
27. Hesperornis and Diatryma.   135
28. Merriam's life zones of North America.   148
29. Biotic provinces of North America.   150
30. Biomes of North America.   152

BIRDS AROUND THE WORLD

Chapter 1

FIRST PRINCIPLES

Why are there Snowy Owls and polar bears in the Arctic but not in the Antarctic? How did the flightless Dodo get to the little island of Mauritius far out in the Indian Ocean, the only place where it occurred? Why do the forests of Brazil teem with hum-

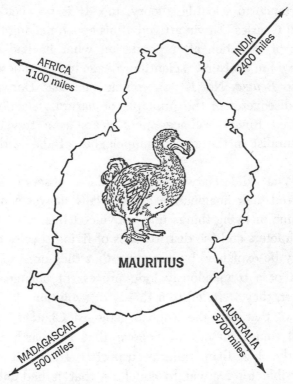

Figure 1. The Dodo. Its ancestors flew to Mauritius; in time they became flightless, and extinction followed when man arrived.

mingbirds, those of the Congo lack a single one? How can a species acquire a distribution as peculiar as that of the Kirtland's Warbler which nests only in a restricted part of Michigan and winters only in the Bahama Islands?

Questions such as these might be asked by the individual whose interest in nature is little more than idle curiosity, but they have been of profound importance to scientific theory, too. It is no accident that Charles Darwin arrived at his epoch-making theory of evolution after pondering what he had observed in a leisurely scientific voyage in His Majesty's Ship *Beagle*. Nor is it a coincidence that Darwin's co-discoverer of the principle of natural selection— Alfred Russel Wallace—spent years as a traveling naturalist in the great archipelagoes of the Middle East.

What did Darwin and Wallace observe that stirred their imaginations? Essentially, it was a panorama of living things that convinced them that the characters and the distributions of living species can only be explained by assuming that they are the result of a tremendously long process of change. In short, they were led to a theory of evolution. At just about that time the English geologist Charles Lyell had found reasons to believe that the earth was vastly older than hitherto suspected. Hence, it was possible for Darwin to conclude that it had taken tens of thousands of years for the little birds of the Galápagos Islands—now called Darwin's Finches—to spread back and forth from island to island, and evolve into the species we now see.

Thus what we may call the classical beginning of modern biology—the era of Darwin and Huxley—had as one of its basic tenets an understanding and interpretation of distribution and often of bird distribution.

After a period of relative neglect, distribution has again become of great importance in evolutionary theory. This is especially true in our understanding of *how* species evolve. This basic question of evolution was only answered when the importance of geographical variation was at last appreciated. This topic—in which T. H. Huxley's grandson, Sir Julian Huxley, and also The American Museum of Natural History's Ernst Mayr, now of Harvard, were pioneers—will be treated in fuller detail later.

What would now be called the ecological aspects of bird distribution—the division into land birds and water birds, arctic birds and tropical birds, and the like—have also been of keen interest as we have tried to suggest by the questions in our first paragraph. And here also recent research has led to a new interest in distribution. In brief, if we can understand why a particular bird is limited to certain areas, to certain habitats and in numbers that fluctuate only within certain limits, we are well on the way to understanding both the bird and its place in nature. These are difficult questions and not yet fully answered for any species, but we are beginning to make progress.

In most books on birds, the ranges are merely descriptive, telling only where the species occur. If there is a section on habits, it will tell something of the bird's requirements or preferences. The purpose of this book is to take such raw data and from them to derive an understanding of the distribution of birds—to answer questions like the ones above.

With few exceptions, each of the 8600 or so species of living birds has a range differing in some respect from that of any other species. We may best begin to understand the reasons for this complexity by postulating a world in which things are simpler. Let us first imagine an earth uniformly covered with one type of landscape, without variation and without climatic zones. For example, grassland might extend from pole to pole around the world. What then would be the distribution of a grassland bird, regardless of where it first evolved? Within a comparatively short period of time, one may safely say, it would spread over this uniform globe and be found everywhere.

Let us now suppose our featureless globe to have a climatic gradient, not as at present with two cold polar regions separated by a warm equatorial one, but rather with one pole cold, the other warm, and with a gradual temperature gradient between. On such a globe one could have arctic species of birds, temperate species, and tropical species. Distribution would still be relatively simple, with all species

Figure 2. On a uniform planet with neither seasons, climate cycles, mountains, nor oceans, birds would be uniformly distributed everywhere.

extending right around the globe in their preferred temperature belt. Already, however, complexities would arise. One temperate species might be more tolerant of cold than another and extend farther into the arctic belt, and so forth.

If we now suppose that temperatures on this hypothetical globe gradually began to fluctuate seasonally in the colder areas, further complications would immediately ensue. Some species would become adapted to the changes and would remain in the same area winter and summer. Others, in an attempt to avoid the winters, would become migratory. Still others would become extinct.

Now suppose this globe to be divided longitudinally—half earth, half ocean, with rocky islands suitable for nesting sea birds scattered uniformly over the ocean. Immediately two classes of birds could exist—sea birds and land birds. Land and water would, with this simple arrangement, not interfere with the distribution of birds. That is to say, no land bird would be kept from suitable habitat by intervening water, or vice versa for the marine species.

We could develop this imaginary globe further but the contrast with the conditions actually existing on the earth will by now be apparent enough. The earth is only so large, the ocean so deep, the mountains so high, and the range of temperatures so great, but within these over-all limitations the existing variations are about the greatest imaginable. Land and water areas vary in size from the continent of Asia or the Pacific Ocean to the smallest islands and ponds. The shape of these land and water masses is irregular and random, as is the presence or absence of islands in the seas. Some mountain ranges and watercourses run north and south and provide convenient migration pathways for birds; others like the Himalayas run east and west and constitute great barriers. The pattern of two cold polar areas separated by a warm equatorial belt means that the earth has two polar and two temperate belts more or less effectively separated by a tropical one.

Small wonder, then, that the distribution of living things is highly complex. But the existence of great geographical diversity is by no means the only complicated part of the problem.

Evolution and Distribution

Until fairly recently many people believed that the earth and the living things on it were created as we now find them in about the year 4000 B.C. Some still do believe it. For them, the facts of distribution, as well as many other matters, are greatly simplified! The species of birds are immutable and the earth itself—rivers, mountains, oceans—though subject to some changes as a result of earthquake or volcano, has altered but little in such a brief span of time. Hence distribution, however complicated, is essentially a static affair. Changes in the abundance of a species, unless the direct result of man's activities, will be regarded as responses to short-term or cyclic changes in weather or other factors that affect distribution.

But things are not so simple. We now know that hundreds of millions of years, rather than a few thousand, have gone into the making of the earth's environments, and that great changes have occurred from time to time. Many of the major mountain chains whose effect on bird evolution and distribution is clear-cut are recent enough to have active volcanoes and frequent earthquakes even today. Islands like the Hawaiian group and the Galápagos, both important to students of distribution, are comparatively recent volcanic upwellings.

Even more important are the great changes in climate which have transformed large parts of the earth's surface from time to time. Coal and other fossils of tropical origin are found in Antarctica and Greenland. As recently as fifteen or twenty thousand years ago great sheets of glacial ice rolled south well into the United States, killing some life, driving other forms southward. Areas that are now vast deserts had ample rain and were covered by forests.

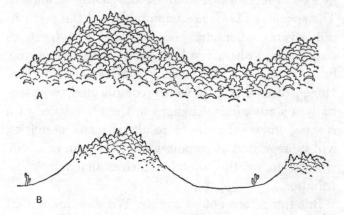

Figure 3. Climatic cycles. A) Humid era—continuous forest. B) Arid era—desert at lower elevations. Such cycles produce range changes and extinction among birds, but also foster the evolution of new species.

The changes in sea level resulting from glaciation and other causes have altered the outlines of islands and continents. North and South America have at times been united by an isthmus of land, at times separated by a strait of water; the same is true of Alaska and Siberia, the British Isles and Europe, and many other areas. All of these changes—some gradual, some sudden—have affected the distribution of birds.

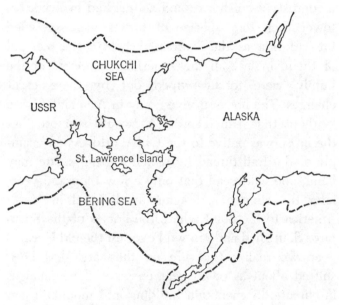

Figure 4. Land bridges. Shallow straits such as that separating Alaska from Siberia have at various times in the past been dry land. Broken line indicates extent of previous land mass. This made dispersal easier, even for birds.

Thus we see that what we find today is the result of millions of years of only partially understood history. Mammals have left more fossils than birds to illuminate this record, so perhaps it is permissible to cite one example from that group. The history of the horse family, which is rather well documented by fossils, shows that horses evolved in North America. From time to time during the 75 million years or so of their existence certain members of the group entered the Old World via Alaskan-Siberian land bridges. By the time of the Pleistocene glaciations modern types of horses and zebras had evolved. No fewer than four species of horses were crowded into Florida as they retreated before the ice. All of them, in fact all the American members of the family, were totally wiped out by these great changes. The horse survived only in Asia and Africa. Without the fossil record, one would suppose that the horse was native to the Old World. As an example of the frail thread by which a group's fate may hang, one will recall that only a few thousand years later the climate had again ameliorated in North America to the point where the horses of the Spaniards flourished and ran wild over all the old West.

So we realize that life on the earth has been shifted about as on a great chessboard by changes in climate, by mountain building and mountain leveling, and by other geological and climatic events. Of equal importance is the fact that birds themselves have also evolved and changed, over a span of perhaps 150 million years. At first there was only one or a few species. By the close of the Eocene or before, some 40 million years ago, the main groups or orders had appeared. Since that time there has been continuous further change; vast numbers of species have become extinct and others have changed beyond recognition. Indeed if we could trace each of the thousands of species of birds back generation by

GEOLOGICAL TIMETABLE OF BIRDS

	RECENT	Man's shattering impact upon the environment

CENOZOIC	PLEISTOCENE (Ice Ages) (1.5 million)		Extinction of many large mammals, some birds; great alterations in ranges and migration
	PLIOCENE (6 million)		Rapid proliferation of songbirds correlated with evolution of flowering plants
	MIOCENE (19 million)		
	OLIGOCENE (12 million)		
	EOCENE (16 million)		Rapid proliferation of modern orders of birds
	PALEOCENE (11 million)		
MESOZOIC	CRETACEOUS (71 million)		Some primitive toothed birds but others becoming modernized
	JURASSIC (59 million)		Transition from reptiles to birds. Archaeopteryx still "half reptile, but feathered."
	TRIASSIC (30 million)		Appearance of reptilian ancestors of birds.

Figure 5.

generation to the Jurassic, some 150 million years ago, they would all converge in one genus, *Archaeopteryx*, or something very like it.

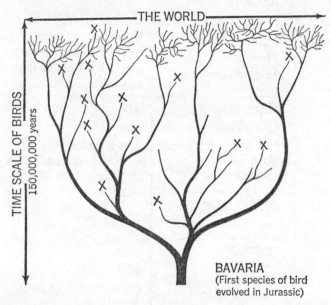

Figure 6. Birds evolved in one place and from one species of reptile; then gradually they spread over the world and diversified. Some types became extinct (X); the distribution of others is still changing.

In studying the distribution of birds, then, one must ask not only what is the present distribution of the species, or group of species, but what was its past distribution and where did it evolve? As we have seen in the case of the horse, the present is not always a trustworthy clue to the past. But unlike the case of the horse, the fossil record for birds is so sketchy that we do not know where most species,

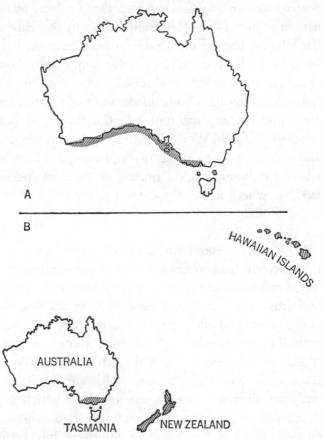

A

B

Figure 7. Present distributions may be very misleading. One subfamily of geese is known today from a single species, the Cape Barren Goose of southern Australia (A). Fossils show that the group was once represented in New Zealand and Hawaii, and probably elsewhere (B).

and even most families, evolved. Sometimes, of course, we can assume that a species evolved where it is now found—the Hawaiian Goose in the Hawaiian Islands, the extinct Dodo on Mauritius, and the Rhea in South America. In a great many cases, however, no such simple deductions are possible. For example, many families of birds, such as parrots, trogons, and barbets, are found in the tropics of both the New and Old Worlds. In such cases, we can only make a guess as to place of origin on the basis of where the family is most numerous, or most specialized, or where it has the closest relatives.

What are the requirements of a particular species? is a question that covers a multitude of complexities. These requirements may vary from season to season, and from place to place, especially in species that vary geographically. Furthermore, "requirements" includes not merely such obvious things as food, water, and shelter, but also the often subtle interactions with competing species, with predators, and with parasites and disease, any or all of which may determine where a species can live and where it cannot. What is the result of all these interacting factors? One may study intensively the distribution of the birds of one locality but he will never be able to find another locality precisely like it. Or he may study the distribution of a single species throughout its entire range, but again, no other species will have exactly the same range and density.

At the outset of this chapter we mentioned the fact that the Himalayas, running east-west, present an impassable barrier to some migratory birds. Let us first, then, turn to such physical barriers, which would seem to be the most clear-cut, if not necessarily the most important, factors in the distribution of birds.

Chapter 2

THE EFFECT OF
PHYSICAL BARRIERS

If one toured the rain forests of Amazonia, West Africa, and New Guinea, he would see that the environment is strikingly similar, the bird life extremely different. The immediate assumption would be that this is a result of physical barriers. It is possible, of course, that certain of the rain-forest species may formerly have been world-wide in their range but now, for a number of complicated reasons, are restricted to just one or the other of the tropical rain-forest areas. But, in the main, the assumption about physical barriers is probably correct.

What is a physical barrier? This may seem like an unnecessary question, but if we define it as any terrain that a given species of animal will not voluntarily cross, certain aspects of bird distribution become clear. First of all, what may be an impassable barrier to a mouse or a hedgehog may be just another small detail in a bird's aerial view of the countryside. It is, in fact, the power of dispersal, the ability of birds to fly, and the varying degrees to which they can overcome physical barriers, that will concern us most in this chapter.

Water and Land

Generally speaking, water is a barrier to land birds, and land a barrier to water birds; forest is a barrier to plains birds and vice versa. The most obvious and basic barrier is water. On a globe three-quarters of which is covered by water one would first of all expect the aquatic or semi-aquatic forms to be more widely dispersed than land birds. Such is usually the case: Ducks, ibises, pelicans, flamingos, and the like have extensive ranges. Sometimes even the same species is to be found on several continents —the Glossy Ibis, a fresh-water bird, is much the same in Florida, Argentina, Hungary, or Australia. At least half of the species of ducks and shore birds of Europe and the United States are the same.

On the other hand, these same two continents share only a few songbirds and these are chiefly swallows which can fly longer distances, especially over water, than most songbirds. Except for a few long-distance migrants, no land birds will *voluntarily* cross wide expanses of water, and because of the irregular conformation of the earth's land surface, water barriers have played a large part in determining the distribution of land birds. Even a big river like the Amazon is a bar to some jungle species of birds, and in the Solomons, islands only two miles apart have different kinds of white-eyes, a small songbird.

Birds that evolved in the Old World may have been able to spread only to the shores of the English Channel, but not to the British Isles, except at those times in the geological past when an isthmus formed across the channel. The same would be true in the case of the Bering Strait, the Isthmus of Panama, and other areas which have at times in the geological past been joined and at other times separated.

But this would not explain the occurrence, on isolated islands and archipelagoes far out at sea, of land birds that we know will not fly the needed distance to reach them. The theory that there once were land bridges from continental land masses to such islands as the West Indies, Hawaii, New Zealand, and Madagascar is now regarded as erroneous, certainly, at least, within the 150-million-year period spanning the geological history of birds.

The theory that the continents once formed one land mass, which then split into continents which later drifted apart, has also been advanced from time to time. South America and Africa, as perennially suggested, have matching coastlines. Even if this did happen, however, it would have been hundreds of millions of years before there were any birds around to witness the event. The geological evidence indicates that during avian history the main outlines of the continents and oceans have been pretty much the same. In that time it has been mountain formation, volcanic action, and especially climatic changes that have brought about great changes in bird distribution, even as recently as the last Ice Age—only yesterday in geological terms.

But this still does not explain how certain land birds have reached distant islands. To be sure, even among land birds one finds an occasional species adapted to moving widely over oceanic archipelagoes. The Pacific Pigeon and the closely allied

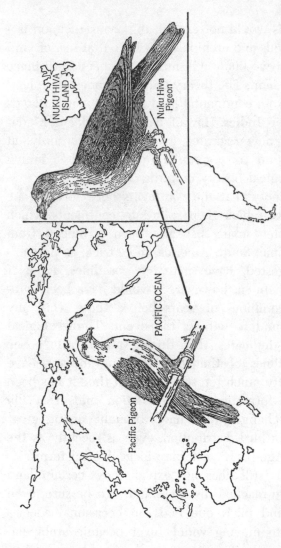

Figure 8. Closely related species may have completely dissimilar patterns of distribution. The widespread Pacific Pigeon occurs on hundreds of islands; the Galeated or Nuku Hiva Pigeon only on one little island.

Micronesian Pigeon inhabit hundreds of scattered islands in the tropical Pacific. Obviously, they wander great distances, yet even in the same genus there are species restricted to single small islands. The most striking example of this is a fine large pigeon confined to the little island of Nuku Hiva in the Marquesas.

Chance

In most cases, the only plausible explanation for island distribution is accidental dispersal, as when a flock of birds is transported by a storm. Bird banders on Fair Isle and other islands off the coast of England have turned up a surprising number of stragglers from North America which, it is believed, became lost at night and were drifted at high altitudes by the prevailing westerlies. Radar indicates that small birds may occasionally be wafted to as high as 20,000 feet.

This is, of course, far more apt to happen to migrants, especially night migrants, than to sedentary species. Furthermore, if a species is to become established in a new area, it is necessary for a pair, if not a small flock, to arrive in good enough condition to survive and nest. Therefore, birds that travel or migrate in flocks, such as starlings or doves, have reached more islands than solitary birds such as woodpeckers. When careful collecting or bird watching is undertaken at almost any spot, but especially on islands and seacoasts, the number of

stragglers encountered is quite remarkable. Very few
of these arrive in pairs or flocks and in good enough
condition to begin nesting. And even the few who
do manage to survive the "trip" will not often find
conditions to their liking. Nevertheless, during the
long course of geological time thousands of accidental colonizations have occurred. One was re-
corded as recently as January 1937. A flock of Fieldfares, a European thrush related to the American
Robin, was blown by a storm from northern Europe
to Greenland. They found conditions to their liking
in southeastern Greenland and the species is now
established there.

On a globe where habitats are so irregularly distributed and where dispersal may be the chance
effect of a storm, the existing distributions will reflect
a large element of chance. The Short-eared Owl,
for example, a widespread continental species, is
found on Hawaii and on the island of Ponape in
the Carolines, but nowhere else in the thousands of
islands in the South Sea archipelagoes. Indeed the
entire faunas of such isolated islands as Hawaii and
New Zealand show the effect of chance distribution
and of varying powers of dispersal. Land mammals,
except flying bats, are usually absent and, among
birds, many families are entirely absent. In Hawaii,
for example, there are no native parrots, doves, or
kingfishers, yet all of these families are represented
on other Polynesian islands.

Volumes have been written about real or alleged
difficulties in explaining the distribution of animals

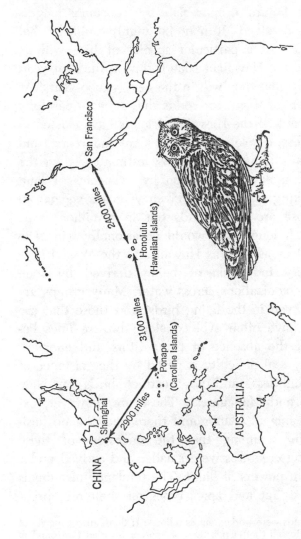

Figure 9. Chance plays a role in distribution. There are thousands of islands in Oceania, but the Short-eared Owl has become established only in Hawaii and on Ponape Island in the Carolines.

and plants, living and fossil. To some extent this is
due to a failure to appreciate the enormous lengths
of time involved. It may be highly unlikely that
individuals of a particular species of bird will be
blown to the Hawaiian Islands during the next year,
but likely that they will in the next 50,000 years! As
a matter of fact, the odds have been carefully
worked out. If the Hawaiian Islands have existed in
their present isolated state for 5 million years (and
some have thought this a low estimate), then the
odds on a new colonization by a species of land
birds taking place in any given year are 333,333 to
1.* Those are heavy odds but in 5 million years
even such long shots would occasionally win. The
fauna of areas such as Hawaii and the West Indies
has every indication of being derived by such
chance colonizations across water. Many groups are
absent, even in the flying birds, and those that are
present have often evolved along bizarre lines because of the absence of competitors and enemies.
The only real difficulty is posed by the existence of
large, flightless, and now extinct birds on New
Zealand and Madagascar. These are, however, extremely ancient islands and there need be no hesi-
tation in assuming that the ancestors of these
lumbering creatures were smaller and arrived under
their own powers of flight. The tendency of animals
to evolve "fat and lazy" types on sheltered, pred-

* The odds were worked out as follows: If there are 15 species of
birds on Hawaii that at one time or another invaded the island in
its 5-million-year history, that means there are 0.3 colonizations
per 100,000 years.

ator-free islands is shown by such additional examples as the Dodo and the Galápagos tortoises.

All birds tend to spread and disperse somewhat, especially the young individuals which, in many species, show no attachment to a particular locality until after they have nested for the first time. In their first year of life, some of the young birds of a given species will spread out beyond the normal range of the species. Thus there is a certain "pressure" tending to expand the range of the species. If the young bird comes against a complete barrier such as the ocean, the range will, to be sure, terminate abruptly. Usually, however, there is a gradual change in the landscape. Thus, as one goes west in North America it gradually becomes drier; forests give way to groves; finally to scattered trees along watercourses. Birds of the eastern forests extend to varying degrees west; those of the western plains to the east.

If we plant trees and build reservoirs, species adapted to this changed environment will quickly appear. A tropical family need have only one or two members more resistant to cold than the others in order to have opportunities for dispersal. Most wrens, for example, are found in the warmer parts of America but the Winter Wren extends far north and at some time crossed the Alaskan-Siberian land bridge. It has since spread across northern Eurasia all the way to the British Isles. The kingfishers are chiefly tropical but our Belted Kingfisher

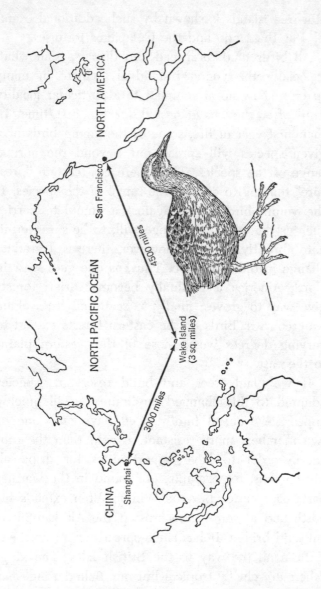

NORTH AMERICA

San Francisco

4,500 miles

NORTH PACIFIC OCEAN

Wake Island
(3 sq. miles)

3,000 miles

CHINA

Shanghai

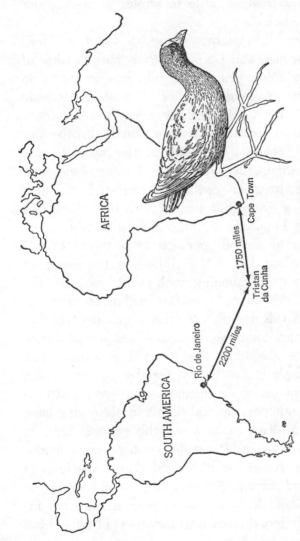

Figure 10. Rails (p. 30), despite their seemingly weak flight, have shown an amazing ability to colonize remote islands, such as Wake Island. Perhaps this is because the young birds disperse at random in all directions. Immature Purple Gallinules (p. 31), caught up in the strong west winds, sometimes are carried all the way to Tristan da Cunha.

AFRICA

SOUTH AMERICA

Rio de Janeiro

Cape Town

Tristan da Cunha

1750 miles

2200 miles

is a hardy creature, able to winter at open water even in Alaska.

Southern, non-migratory species like the Cardinal, Bobwhite, and Carolina Wren push northward whenever a few years with mild winters follow in succession. A severe winter may then decimate these outposts but, in this way, even the most sedentary species tend to enlarge their distributions whenever conditions permit. A few species, such as sand grouse and the Rosy Starling, have lemming-like irregular outbreaks triggered by food shortage or overpopulation. At such times they may penetrate hundreds of miles into unsuitable territory, only to die off, perhaps after trying to rest once or twice. But if the climate or the nature of the landscape is changing, such events may, over the long run, bring about a marked expansion of range.

Finally, it is desirable to stress again the fact that a species must not only be able to reach a new area, it must be able to survive when it gets there. The best example of this is provided by the rail family. Dependent, as many of them are, upon scattered marshes, random dispersal flights by the young have evolved at least in some of the genera. This, of course, results in a certain wastage of individuals but increases the likelihood that a species will spread and survive. For example, individuals of the Purple Gallinule in immature plumage are not infrequently found on islands hundreds of miles from the nearest breeding area of the species in South America. Indeed such occurrences were so regular

on Tristan da Cunha (which is actually nearer to
Africa) that it was supposed that the species must
be established there as a breeder. It is not, but
many other rails have succeeded in colonizing remote islands. For example, the only non-marine
bird on tiny Wake Island was a species of rail found
nowhere else. It was exterminated by the starving,
bypassed Japanese garrison in World War II.

Introduced Species

Indirect but unmistakable evidence of the great
importance of physical barriers upon distribution is
provided by the sensational success of some species
introduced into new environments by man. A few
pairs of House Sparrows and of Starlings were un-
wisely introduced into the New York area from
Europe about the turn of the century. Both have
since spread from coast to coast and today the
Starling may well be the most abundant bird in
North America. Other introduced species that have
succeeded at least locally in North America are the
Pheasant, the Chukar Partridge, and the Hungarian
Partridge. On the other hand, various European
songbirds have failed to become established, or have
done so very locally, sometimes lingering for a few
decades, only to die out at last. Introduced at about
the same time as the House Sparrow, the European
Goldfinch lasted until about 1950, the last few pairs
disappearing when their haunts near Massapequa,
Long Island, succumbed to the bulldozer. On the

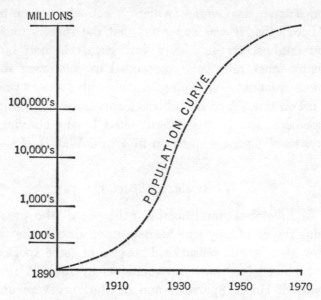

Figure 11. "Population explosion" of the Starling in North America after its introduction in 1890. Its increase has resulted in a decrease in some other species.

other hand, the California House Finch, when turned loose in Long Island about 1950, immediately thrived, now exists by the thousands, and is spreading into New Jersey. It may well be, however, that it could not survive without winter feeding stations.

A species that fails to do well on a large continent where competition and predators are old and entrenched may flourish in an insular environment. New Zealand swarms with various songbirds brought over from England by the settlers. Thrushes, Blackbirds, and finches abound while Skylarks have become a pest in croplands. Even the Australian Black Swan, which had not reached New Zealand under its own power, on being introduced became abundant and now threatens to crowd out native waterfowl. On the Hawaiian Islands absolutely no native songbirds are left in the groves and parks in the lowlands. Their places have been taken by a motley assemblage of introduced white-eyes, babblers, cardinals, and weaver finches, all of which are overshadowed by screeching mynahs from India. One must ascend into the mountains to see such remnants as remain of the unique original bird life of the forests.

The distinction between physical and ecological barriers is one of degree and extent. Even the ocean may be regarded as an ecological barrier—it is too *wet* for land birds! In East Africa, flamingos frequent shallow salt lakes, never the surrounding bush and desert. They do, however, fly across such country for scores or hundreds of miles, so it is not an effective barrier to their distribution. If, however, two lakes were so far apart that the birds could not or would not fly from one to the other, then a physical (or geographic) barrier would exist. It may well be that the two species of Andean flamingos would thrive on the high lakes of central Asia. However, the thousands of miles of intervening unsuitable land and water effectively prevent them from reaching that area. The wide expanse of warm tropical

waters that have kept the penguins from reaching
the Arctic illustrate perfectly that a physical barrier
is sometimes merely an ecological barrier of wide
extent.

Chapter 3

ECOLOGICAL REQUIREMENTS

Each species of bird evolved, obviously, in an area that met its needs. How far it later spread and the limits of its range today are subject to a great many variable factors. It is true, however, that all living species will tend to spread and multiply until their numbers represent all that the environment will support. To be sure, cycles of unfavorable years (or centuries) have exterminated some species and resulted in a conservative rate of reproduction in others.

Food and Water

The first and most basic requirement of birds is food and water, and we must bear in mind that food requirements may vary seasonally and usually are different for very young birds. Some birds, such as swallows, eat only insects but can fly widely over forest, orchard, meadow, or river catching them. Others, such as the Woodcock, which probes for worms in swamps, or the Everglade Kite, which feeds only on one genus of fresh-water snails, are much more restricted in food requirements and, therefore, locale. Most birds, however, eat a fairly wide variety of food—some, such as crows, being highly omnivorous—and it is not unusual for birds to wander rather widely in search of food. In the tropics a flowering or fruiting tree is often continuously full of a variety of birds, while one may search in vain for them elsewhere. Hummingbirds seek the first flowers in valleys and ascend the mountains as the summer advances.

When nesting, birds are, perforce, tied down to a smaller area. If they are too crowded at that season they may be unable to secure enough food for their young. As a result, a "nesting territory" has evolved in many species. Each pair excludes other members of the same species from its territory. When food is abundant the territories become smaller, but they have an irreducible minimum.

A pair of eagles may have a territory covering several square miles, while an acre or two is enough for a pair of wrens. But the eagles require about five months to raise a family and they hunt fairly large animals which would soon become scarce or wary if the eagles confined their hunting to a small area. The wrens, on the other hand, feed on spiders and insects which occur by the thousands in a single acre. Furthermore, the young wrens leave the nest when only two weeks old.

Of course, territory has other functions as well but it does act to conserve the food supply of many birds during the critical nesting period. Indeed some species maintain a food territory throughout the year. In the non-breeding season it is often each bird for itself but sometimes the pair merely remains in the nesting territory. This is true of the Red-tailed Hawk in California. If another Red-tail appears it is promptly chased out of the region by the resident pair. Clearly this sets a limit on the population size and it also tends to push surplus birds into less suitable terrain and thus keep the distribution of the species at its maximum extent.

Some migratory birds have winter feeding territories far from their summer homes. Thus a Nightingale that nested in Germany may set up a winter territory in an Egyptian garden.

One might argue that a bird will have to compete for its food supply with other species as well as its own. This is true. To some extent territorial behavior, insofar as it affects food supply, is directed toward other species as well. Anyone who has a feeding station has observed that the bigger and more aggressive species such as Blue Jays and Starlings eat first—the others take what is left, if anything. The same thing holds true for natural foods but is more difficult to detect. Nectar-feeding species such as hummingbirds are an exception and are easily seen to be very aggressive toward any other birds that approach their favorite flowers. Clearly these pressures for food—whether territorial or not strictly so—play a very important role in distribution. In fact they are probably the reason why some birds are rare or local or even why they have become extinct.

Water is usually not such a stringent necessity as food because a great many birds obtain enough by eating insects and fruit. But those eating dry seeds, for example, have more of a problem. When such birds—finches, parrots, and doves—live in deserts, they must fly long distances to find water to drink once or twice each day.

In central Australia, just at sundown, the Flock Pigeons come in the thousands to a water hole. Then they may move to another area and not one will be seen at the former site. Obviously the distribution of such birds is stringently controlled by the availability of water. They can be greatly affected by long-term droughts. This pigeon was once reputed to be extinct but following a rainy season or two it reappeared and increased tremendously. Somewhat similar is the familiar Parakeet, or "Budgie," whose status near Alice Springs in central Australia may vary from complete absence to great abundance.

Recent research has shown that some of these desert birds are becoming physiologically adapted to arid regions. A Budgie can get along much better on a reduced water intake than most birds of its size. In fact, if it has shade and is allowed to be somewhat inactive, it can live for weeks with no water at all beyond that which it gets from a diet of dry seeds. Of course, even the dry seeds contain a little water.

What about marine birds? We know that a human on a life raft in the ocean is doomed unless he has a supply of fresh water. The average bird or mammal is simply not equipped to survive on salt water. Strictly marine birds such as albatrosses have become adjusted to this problem. Special salt glands emptying through the nostrils excrete salt from the blood in the form of very concentrated brine. Thus they can drink all the salt water they want. Presumably such birds as jaegers and phalaropes are adjusted to fresh water in the summer, salt in the winter when they are on the high seas. It is possible, however, that they get most of the necessary fluids from their food and actually take in very little salt water. Some birds that inhabit very brackish waters do go to fresh springs to drink and bathe. Flamingos of the intensely alkaline lakes of central Africa may be observed doing this, but we do not know whether it is a daily process for each bird.

Shelter

Turning now to the need for a secure place to roost at night, and at the proper season, to build a nest and lay eggs, we again find a tremendous range of requirements. Many birds—wrens, quail, marsh birds, and others—are completely dependent upon dense vegetation and can scarcely be driven from it. If such species migrate they do so at night, as they do not wish to be exposed to their enemies in the glare of broad daylight.

The late Professor Paul L. Errington of Iowa State University found that cover and shelter are strictly correlated with abundance and distribution of a bird such as the Bobwhite. If the cover is poor the birds are exposed to predators and the population is reduced to the number having adequate shelter. Since cover and food are at their scantiest in late winter, that is the period when the population

reaches its lowest ebb. Of course some birds—gulls, ducks, swallows, and songbirds such as the American Robin, for example—can usually elude their enemies and are abundant and conspicuous in the open.

We have already pointed out that providing food for the young in the nest presents a special problem, partly solved in some instances by territorial behavior. Likewise the matter of adequate shelter for nest and young is a critical factor for many birds that have no problems of this nature at other seasons. Many ducks have few enemies other than man when adult but a great many when nesting. In some parts of Canada crows rob most of the early duck nests but the ducks re-nest and as the vegetation is by then ranker, success is greater. The brooding ducks are often caught by foxes; this is believed to be one reason males outnumber females in some waterfowl.

It is worth mentioning one or two examples of nesting requirements that directly affect distribution. The Belted Kingfisher must have a vertical bank in which to excavate its nesting burrow. The Screech Owl cannot nest unless it finds a suitable cavity in a tree. The widespread Peregrine Falcon is generally dependent upon cliffs and is absent as a nesting bird from many districts that are suitable

Figure 12. A species must be able to survive the worst, or critical, season of the year. Bobwhites, for example, suffer most from predators in winter when the plant cover is sparse; when land is cleared for farming, they may disappear completely.

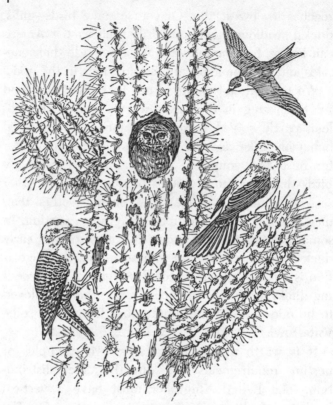

Figure 13. Some birds compete for nesting sites. The wood-pecker (left) dug the hole; the owl pre-empted it; the fly-catcher (right) and the swallow (top right) would like to nest in it.

in every other respect. In the desert the frequent presence in lone trees of nests of eagles or ravens shows how great is the demand for a site secure from ground predators. Some swifts are very demanding—they require niches in a cliff behind a waterfall. The Cliff Swallows of Capistrano—and elsewhere—build nests of clay. They nest only where mud puddles are a convenient source of material. Flamingos must have precisely the right water levels to nest. They may be able to breed only at intervals of several years or they may fly many miles to a more suitable area. Even so, too rapid drying of the nesting area or other changes may mean the loss of thousand of eggs or chicks. At a recent nesting at Lake Magadi in Africa, the drying waters became so saline that nodules of salt formed on the chicks' legs, killing those that were not rescued by man.

Perhaps the clearest and most dramatic example of the need for a nesting place as a determinant of distribution is provided by certain oceanic birds, like albatrosses, petrels, and penguins. These birds spend most of their lives at sea, but must return to land to nest. At the proper season, scattered oceanic islands like Midway in the Central Pacific will be the crowded scene of nesting activity. Sooty Terns and Laysan Albatrosses will be found nesting directly on the sand; others, like the Frigate-birds, build nests in the bushes; still others deposit their eggs in burrows in the turf. After the nesting season, when the fledglings are on their own, the birds again take to the sea.

Albatrosses and petrels can roost on the water; they need come ashore only to nest. Thus, the Wandering Albatross, largest of flying birds, can range for thousands of miles without touching land. On the other hand, some sea birds, such as the Frigatebird, cannot or will not roost on the water and their distribution is thus limited to the distance they can range from shore.

Many birds that nest in isolated pairs roost during the winter in large flocks. In some parts of the world, flights of gulls, parrots, vultures, and blackbirds, to name only a few, are a conspicuous feature on their way to roost. Each winter evening in Manhattan thousands of Starlings can be seen thronging to a single roost beneath an elevated highway, and elsewhere accumulations of Tree Swallows, Redwinged Blackbirds, and Crows may be equally large. In some birds, the winter range is in part determined by the availability of suitable places for such social roosts.

Another place where roosting sites are important is the far north. The nights are long and frigid; small birds can find scarcely enough to eat to keep their body temperature up to normal—a high 100° F. —from dusk to dawn. With very few exceptions the only small birds to winter in such latitudes are chickadees and others which roost in holes in trees. These are cold enough, but not as bad as outside on a twig.

Water, so long as it is open, is, of course, less cold than the air, at least for a bird that is insulated by a layer of fat and a coat of oily waterproof feathers. One observer watched Eider Ducks wintering in open leads in the sea ice off Greenland at a time when the temperatures were forty degrees or so below zero. When these birds took wing they immediately shook themselves vigorously in flight, and instantly got rid of the water on the plumage. Occasionally, one of the Eiders would be in poor condition, through lack of food. Ice would begin to form on its plumage when it took flight and in a few minutes it would be frozen as stiff as though it had been in a deep-freeze locker for a week. It is indeed remarkable that any bird has become adapted to find food and shelter under such conditions!

Migration

In any account of birds and their requirements in relation to distribution, the flexibility resulting from their powers of flight is always apparent. The most extreme example of this is provided by migration.

In many parts of the globe a great percentage of the bird species is migratory; this includes Europe and North America in which natural history has been most actively pursued and for which our knowledge is greatest. Other groups of animals either do not migrate or, like mammals, fish, and butterflies, have only a relatively small number of migratory species.

Seasonal changes in weather characterize many parts of the globe. Of such changes by all odds the most important are those correlated with winter and summer in the colder parts of the world. During the short arctic summer the tundra is covered with pools which teem with the larvae of mosquitoes

Figure 14. Seasonal changes have a tremendous effect on bird distribution; this is most pronounced in the polar regions. Compare these views of the tundra in summer and winter.

and other aquatic life. At that time the northland can support countless individuals and numerous species of shore birds, ducks, geese, swans, cranes, and jaegers. In winter these same tundras are frozen solid and swept by icy gales. The only birds that can survive are ptarmigan, which browse on the low vegetation, and an occasional Snowy Owl or Raven. The shore birds have fled, many of them to such very distant wintering grounds as New Zealand or the coasts of Chile. The arctic areas are as different in winter and summer as day and night; as one enters the temperate regions, winter is less extreme but is still very pronounced, even in the northern half of the United States, and especially in areas of deciduous forest. In summer the abundant insect life supports a variety of swallows, flycatchers, cuckoos, and warblers; in winter the only insectivorous birds are a few woodpeckers and nuthatches that are prepared to dig out hidden grubs from the leafless, "dead" trees.

How did migration evolve? Even resident species often have slightly different home ranges in winter and in summer, or in the breeding and the non-breeding season. As we have seen they may be more "tied down" when raising a family, or they may have to seek out a particular kind of nest site.

Species that have different foods at different seasons are apt to travel about in search of them. From these relatively short and local wanderings it is only a step-by-step progression to more extensive travels. The latter are usually synchronized with seasonal changes—wet and dry seasons, or winter and summer.

Even in the tropics it is remarkable how many birds are migratory. The late Dr. James P. Chapin of The American Museum of Natural History demonstrated this for many African species. The Pennant-winged Nightjar, for example, breeds only in the African savannas south of the equator. It then migrates to the grasslands north of the Congo for-

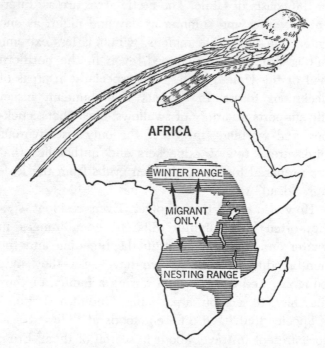

Figure 15. Purely tropical birds such as the African Pennant-winged Nightjar often have definite migrations. In this case it enables the bird to avoid prolonged dry seasons when its insect food is scarce. After J. P. Chapin.

ests. In this way it resides in each region during the season of rains, when the flying insects upon which it subsists are abundant. This is just as truly a migration as that of a bird that nests in Canada and winters in Central America.

Only a relatively few birds wander widely but irregularly. One of these exceptions is the African Wattled Starling. It wanders about in great flocks following the migratory locusts. When the locusts stop in a suitable area to lay their eggs, the starlings stop too and feed their young on the wingless young hoppers.

Migratory birds, almost without exception, breed in only one of their two seasonal homes. Northern birds nest in their summer home and not in their tropical "winter resort." Even tropical migrants nest in only one area. This does not necessarily imply that the nesting area is ancestral for the species. The Scarlet Tanager which nests in southern Canada surely spread to this northern area after the last glaciation a few thousand years ago. Almost all of its relatives are tropical. On the other hand, if one of several petrels nesting in the southern hemisphere migrates into the North Atlantic, it is apparently a case of having gradually extended the range farther and farther from the nesting area.

Thus migration may affect distribution profoundly. This was especially true during the Ice Ages, as already suggested for the Scarlet Tanager. At that time northern areas became less and less suitable for nesting birds, but at the same time many formerly subtropical areas, because of the drop in temperature, became more favorable for northern birds. When the ice retreated birds tended to retrace their way north. Some of them, however, had become "stranded" on southern islands or mountaintops, and remained there. Examples are the White-winged Crossbill on the peaks of Haiti, a kinglet on Formosa, and a crossbill and bullfinch in the mountains of northern Luzon.

It is easy to see why swallows depart from Alaska in winter, less obvious why they should return each summer. If, however, they remained in the tropics they would have to compete during the nesting season with many resident, southern birds. And the north is as rich in insects during the summer as it is poor in winter. One would *expect* many birds to take advantage of the lush northern summer, and such, in fact, is what we do find.

Thus one cannot make a single generalization about the origin or former ranges of migratory birds vis-à-vis the winter or summer quarters. Living organisms are opportunists. Nature abhors a vacuum; birds usually have succeeded in colonizing suitable areas in one way or another.

Anyone investigating the ecological factors limiting the distribution of species will do well to consider the versatility of many migratory ones. Baltimore Orioles and Rose-breasted Grosbeaks, which nest in eastern groves and orchards, winter in Amazonian jungles—really a very different type of environment. The Red Phalarope nests on the tundra, winters on the high seas. In analyzing such seasonal differences one thinks first of the environment required during the nesting season. This may, in some species, reflect the needs of the nestlings, rather than of the adults. In passing we may note again that non-migratory birds also adjust in various ways to the different conditions of winter and summer. In winter they may have different food, roosting places, and social habits. Starlings and American Crows, for example, have immense winter roosts, but are solitary when nesting. Kestrels eat grasshoppers in the summer, mice in the winter.

Migration is thus an adaptation that enables birds to survive by shifting their ranges from season to season. These movements have an effect on the birds that do not migrate, as well as those that do, in that they influence the number of species and individuals competing for the available food supply at any particular time and place. The north has many advantages for nesting birds—long days, rich insect life, relatively few predators. These offset the hazards of migration and of wintering in distant areas.

The Ecological Niche

The sum total of a bird's demands upon the environment comprises what is known as its "ecological niche." If we could describe the exact set of conditions under which a species thrives best, that would be its ecological niche. Since it reflects not only the positive requirements of the species but also such negative factors as disease, parasites, predators, and competition, the ecological niche is very complex, never fully known for any species, and, indeed, to some extent a theoretical, idealistic concept. That is to say, a species might do even better in some other ecological niche (which may or may not exist elsewhere on the globe). Indeed one may say categorically that it would do better in a niche that gave it more food, and greater security from enemies and parasites. A songbird may live twelve

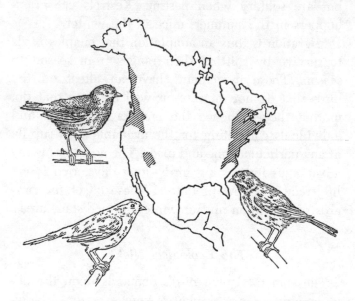

Figure 16. Some birds live in rather distinct environments in various parts of their range and often show adaptations to these regional conditions. Thus in the Song Sparrow, desert populations are pale; those of the rain-swept coastal forests of British Columbia are dark; and the subspecies of the eastern part of the continent is intermediate.

years in a cage while very few attain half that age in the wild. Is the cage a better ecological niche for such a species? Perhaps, but nature provides no cages.

One may also note that a species' ecological niche is not exactly the same in different regions. The Song Sparrow lives in brackish marshes along San Francisco Bay; in backyard currant bushes in New England; among the rocks and tussock grass along the shores of the Aleutian Islands. In migratory birds the niche may differ drastically in winter and summer, as emphasized previously.

Some species have a much broader tolerance than others. In general these will be the more abundant, "successful," and widespread species. One thinks of the Crow, the Robin, and the Starling. On the other hand, the Ivory-billed Woodpecker requires large stands of virgin swampy cypress timber. Since these no longer exist this woodpecker is extinct or virtually so. It is, to be sure, possible to find specialized birds that do thrive in large numbers. Still, they remain more susceptible to changes in the environment than do other birds.

It is easy to form a general impression of a bird's ecological niche. The Yellow-headed Blackbird, for example, nests in fresh-water marshes, usually in rushes standing in water, in western United States and adjacent southern Canada. Most of that region is more or less arid; such marshes are widely scattered and so is the occurrence of this bird. It reaches its eastern limit in central Wisconsin where it is present, in small numbers, in a few marshes but absent from others that look suitable. What is it that has kept it from ranging farther east? Food? Some parasite associated with moister eastern climates? No one knows.

The ecological niche, then, reflects much that is

Figure 17. The Sandhill Crane requires a fresh-water marsh for nesting, the water and vegetation providing protection for the nest. Each species has such an "ecological niche."

subtle, along with the more obvious. In particular, interactions among species are often all-important, but exceedingly hard to assess. This matter is discussed in Chapter 5 but it is worthwhile to cite an example or two here. In East Africa one species of thrush of the genus *Cossypha* is found in lowland forests and another in mountain forests. Nothing could be more natural than to assume that the first species is adapted to the lowlands and cannot live in the mountains. Yet, on one peak where the mountain species does not occur, the lowland one extends to the top of the mountain! The truth is, therefore, that the lowland thrush can and does live on mountains, provided it does not have to compete with the better adapted mountain species. Similarly, in British Columbia the Varied Thrush seems to be restricted to certain nesting habitats by its aggressive relative, the Robin.

It should be evident from the above that we do not know everything about the "ecological niche" (and hence about the distribution) of any bird and never will. We can never fully know, for instance, what the effect would be on the Hairy Woodpecker if the Downy Woodpecker did not exist. On the other hand, we do know a great deal about a few species. Some of the game birds, in particular, have been intensively studied. In his book *The Canvasback on a Prairie Marsh*, Dr. H. A. Hochbaum has analyzed the environmental needs of the most celebrated of American sporting wildfowl. Another game bird, the Ruffed Grouse, has been of interest because of its sharp cycles of abundance and rarity which occur more or less regularly every few years. The reason for these is still a matter of debate. Probably it is a combination of factors that ensues when the population becomes too great—disease, food shortage, and possibly malfunction of the endocrine system resulting from stress.

How does a species recognize its ecological niche? The reaction is at least partly innate or "instinctive." It has, during the evolution of the species, become ingrained in the heredity. Hence we speak of taking to something "as a duck takes to water." Some preliminary experiments have been carried out to determine in what way the bird recognizes or selects its favored habitat, and also to determine to what extent it is hereditary and to what extent learned. Adult wild Chipping Sparrows, when offered a choice in an aviary, preferred pine to oak boughs for shelter. Young of the same species, however, when reared in a box lined with oak leaves, showed a much greater tolerance of oak. Thus the preference for pine is not so ingrained that it cannot be modified or conditioned. This was to be expected. A bird resident the year around in a particular habitat will probably be more limited and exacting in its choices than migrants or species that normally wander widely.

In other words, birds select their habitat in large part by an innate, "psychological" process. The young Cowbird is often reared in the woods by a Vireo or Ovenbird. But as soon as the young impos-

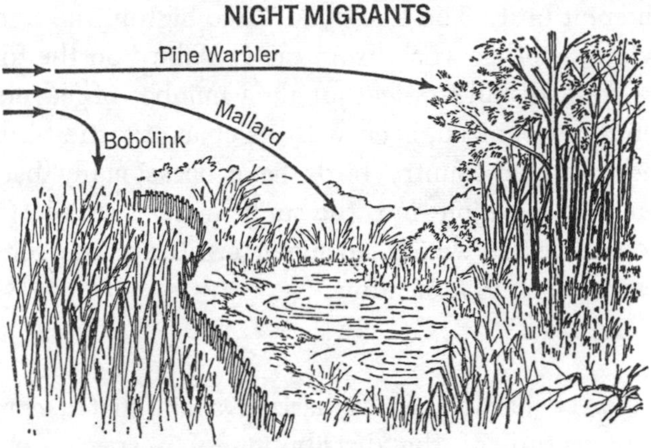

NIGHT MIGRANTS

Figure 18. Most species of birds instinctively select a type of habitat to which they have become adapted. At the end of a night's flight, ducks settle in water, bobolinks in grassland, and pine warblers in a grove of pines.

tor (the species is a brood parasite) is independent of its foster parents it unerringly seeks out other Cowbirds living in flocks in open country. Animals, including birds, have evolved nervous systems to enable them to be conscious of their environment; it is no surprise that these nervous systems have acquired patterns or "grooves" that tend to keep a species in the niche to which, as a result of hundreds of thousands of years of adjustment, it is best adapted.

Usually when we classify birds ecologically we are thinking in "horizontal" or topographic terms. We pass from a prairie to a marsh and encounter a new group of birds. In forests there is also a "vertical" distribution of habitats or niches, which attract different birds. The Red-eyed Vireo high in the trees lives in another world from the Ovenbird on the forest floor. In tall tropical jungle a number of "layers" can be recognized, each with its characteristic birds. Indeed, open-country birds have occasionally been found to move out into the sunlit upper surface of a tropical forest, which, to flying creatures, has some resemblance to a meadow.

It need hardly be emphasized again that a complete picture of the distribution of a species will include an assessment of when and where it evolved and of geographical and seasonal differences in its ecological niche. However, it is perhaps fair to say that, at the moment, intense ecological study of a species in one area, and usually at the nesting season, employing experimental methods where possible, is the most active field of research as regards the problems involving distribution.

Chapter 4

HARMFUL AND BENEFICIAL FACTORS

In the last chapter we discussed some requirements of birds and how they affect distribution. Here we shall consider factors inimical to birds. They have many enemies, including some members of their own group—hawks, owls, shrikes, and crows. Flight itself is probably an adaptation to escape these and other dangers. Nevertheless many adult birds are caught by predators, and the toll of eggs and young is great. To measure the effect of such predation upon bird distribution is a difficult task. About all we can say is that when a species is declining for some reason, predation may act as another push in the direction of extinction.

Predators and Parasites

Some ground-feeding birds have lost the power of flight apparently because they inhabit islands where there are no predators. The Dodo is a classic example and one thinks also of various flightless insular species of rails and the kiwis of New Zealand. Disaster often overtook such species when man arrived with his menage of dogs, cats, and swine, not to mention guns and snares. Wild predators have sometimes reached islands by normal means of dispersal and exterminated the native fauna in similar fashion. We may safely assume that many albatrosses, petrels, and other species that nest on islands lacking carnivorous mammals would be more widespread were it not for the presence of such enemies on continents. In Peru, when a predator-proof wall was built across the base of a peninsula, sea birds previously confined to islands began to nest there. Hence predation has a very important influence upon distribution.

Much the same may be said of parasites. Ordinarily a balance has been reached by millions of years of interaction between parasite and host. If, however, an individual (or a population) is weakened by disease or malnutrition, it may become more heavily infested with parasites and succumb to a combination of factors. The boundaries of a bird's range may sometimes be determined by differences in the frequency of a parasite. In California during unusually rainy years nests of Red-tailed Hawks

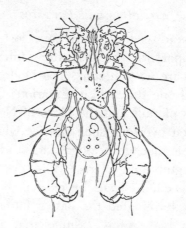

Figure 19. Parasites such as this formidable-looking feather mite—here greatly magnified—sometimes restrict a species' range. After T. Clay and M. Rothschild.

were infested by a bloodsucking fly. Swarms of these pests were visible above the nests and some of the young hawks succumbed to their attacks. The absence of such a hawk in certain humid areas might be due to the greater prevalence of this parasite. Speaking more generally, is it not likely that changes in climate have sometimes led to extinction by upsetting such delicate balances between parasite and host? And as always, a species of limited range, especially one confined to an island, will be most apt to suffer such a fate.

What has been said of parasites will be equally true of disease; indeed bacteria and viruses are "parasites." We have seen the American chestnut nearly wiped out by Asiatic blight and the rabbit decimated in Europe and Australia by myxomatosis. In both cases the plague did stop short of total extinction and a resistant strain may someday evolve. But these were widespread species with millions of individuals; certainly rare or local species might be exterminated in short order by such a disease. Indeed some scientists believe that the extinction of several Hawaiian birds was caused by the introduction of avian malaria and the mosquitoes which spread it.

Climate

Great changes in climate have occurred from time to time during geological history, thereby producing equally great changes in the fauna and flora. One of these upheavals came at the end of the Cretaceous period. The Age of Reptiles, which had lasted for millions of years, was over. A rapid evolution of flowering plants, birds, and mammals ensued. The climatic fluctuations that occurred during the Ice Ages at the close of the Pleistocene period produced changes that were almost as dramatic, and because they were so much nearer in time they are easier to interpret. Indeed dating of fossils by the radioactive method using Carbon 14 has shown that the last great ice sheet may have covered the northern United States as recently as 12,000 years ago. One might tend to think that these vast climatic pulsations would have only a temporary effect on bird distribution. However, as we showed in discussing migration, some species were driven south by the ice and cold, became stranded on southern mountains, and have remained there to this day. Others became extinct.

The effect of glaciation on mammals was more severe than upon birds. Before the glaciation North America was the home of mammoths, mastodons, rhinoceroses, camels, and giant ground sloths. It was indeed, as Professor Henry Fairfield Osborn proclaimed, the Golden Age of Mammals. This age ended with the advance of the ice. Not only the mammals but many birds, such as the great vultures, died out along with the beasts, upon whose carcasses they had preyed. Nevertheless, the effect of the glacial epochs was much less disastrous for birds than for mammals: They swarmed back into the northern localities as soon as the summers were warm enough to provide food.

Coming down to the present, it is difficult to point to patterns of distribution among birds that are a *direct* result of climate. Most birds do not exhibit obvious external adaptations to heat or cold. The bareheaded King Vulture of Amazonia with its fleshy head-wattles could not, of course, live in northern Canada during the winter. Likewise, the dense feathering, extending down onto the toes, of the Snowy Owl and Ptarmigan of the Arctic is surely an adaptation to withstand cold. Nevertheless, we see very few external adaptations as between a wintering chickadee and a flycatcher that migrates before the first frosts. Zoo keepers tell us that some tropical birds can tolerate cold so long as they have plenty to eat; others are more sensitive.

Considering birds as a group, one is impressed by their ability to survive all extremes of climate and weather. The Emperor Penguin, as an example, goes without food for as long as a month while incubating its egg during the depth of the antarctic winter. How can it maintain a body temperature of about 100°F. for that length of time, without food? The thick layer of "blubber" it has at the beginning of this fast is certainly essential.

Turning to climatic events of more limited impact, what is the effect of storms, cold, or dry spells affecting only one season? However severe locally, their impact on distribution is usually not of long duration. But when a bird has a very small range, it can be wiped out by a single storm. Some years ago, there was concern that the Cape Sable Seaside Sparrow of the southern tip of Florida had been wiped out by a severe hurricane. The Eastern Bluebird has been evicted from most of its nesting sites by the introduced Starling and has declined greatly. When the decimation of an unusually severe winter was added to this, disaster threatened. Fortunately this favorite bird of so many has been able to make a comeback, though very slowly.

As we have mentioned earlier, storms may also have a positive role in distribution by scattering birds far and wide.

Man's Impact

Man's impact on the environment has been tremendous, and at times catastrophic. It is, of course, becoming more so every day as the human population becomes greater and the dubious benefits of mechanization, chemistry, and now atomic power are bestowed upon the entire globe. Birds are part of the environment and, like the rest of it, have been profoundly affected by such activities.

Some believe that man was able to part company with the other primates when he began to hunt in groups, using a spear as a weapon. At any rate early man was definitely a hunter. Yet there is no reason to believe that his activities posed any great threat to wildlife. Exceptionally, the case may have been otherwise. In New Zealand, the clumsy, flightless moas, already on their way out because of the climatic ups and downs of the Pleistocene, were pushed over the brink when the first natives reached these islands. The same may have been true of that most ponderous bird of all, the Elephant-bird of Madagascar. We are not sure whether or not it still existed when *Homo sapiens* first stepped from an outrigger canoe onto the beaches of this great island.

But it was not until rather modern times that man's impact on the environment really became profound. The industrial revolution, large-scale agriculture and attendant destruction of forests, settling of the "new" continents, and, more recently, rampant use of chemical fertilizers and pesticides are among the factors involved. Dozens of species of birds have become extinct, and vastly more have decreased in numbers and disappeared from many areas. The process has not halted but is accelerating, impelled by the population explosion. One can only hope that modern man will not destroy his environment as effectively as the Mayas and some other vanished civilizations succeeded in doing. Birds are scarcely more than a pawn in these global reverberations. But as with the caged canaries once used to warn of poison gas in coal mines, we may by saving nature save mankind.

Beneficial Factors

Man's influence upon birds is by no means entirely detrimental. Today the colorful Cardinal occurs in the northeastern states in far greater numbers than ever before. Why? Primarily, it would seem, because bird-feeders have become standard backyard equipment in suburbia. Severe winters no longer decimate this and other semi-hardy species. And the profusion of ornamental shrubs provides nesting places.

In the rural areas, hundreds of farm ponds have been built under a program sponsored by the federal government. On a far larger scale the vast series of dams built by the Reclamation Service for irrigation and water power has provided habitats for many water birds. The irrigated fields themselves, bordered by shrubs, have far more birds per square mile than the surrounding desert. Several pairs of eastern and western species, long separated by the plains and deserts of the interior, have followed agriculture and windbreaks across the prairies. When the members of such pairs which evolved in isolation meet, they often interbreed to varying extents. Examples are the Bullock's and Baltimore orioles, the Lazuli and Indigo buntings, the Black-headed and the Rose-breasted grosbeaks. In such cases, changes in the landscape caused by man have not only led to great expansions of range but have altered the course of evolution.

To be sure, such changes have displaced some species while helping others, but at least one may say that there are often as many or more birds as previously. For a student of distribution such transformations are of very considerable interest. Even sea birds have sometimes been aided by civilization. The vast numbers of gulls attracted to land fills and garbage dumps around big seaports are a common sight. When the British fishing fleet began to clean their catch at sea and dump the offal overboard it produced a tremendous increase in the Fulmar Petrel. As its numbers swelled, the range expanded. New nesting colonies were established. Often the first birds in such nesting colonies of sea birds are young individuals, unable to secure a nesting place in the older established colonies.

In the future one may assume that a growing human population will make it mandatory to set up adequate watersheds, to prevent pollution of streams and rivers, and to control the use of chemicals. This will benefit birds and other wildlife and to varying degrees, one hopes, offset the seemingly inevitable advance of parking lots and concrete highways.

Chapter 5

SPECIES DYNAMICS AND DISTRIBUTION

Birds, like other living things, are of many distinct kinds. These we call species. The differences between them are often obvious and apparent to everyone. The American Indian did not need a scientist to tell him that the Wild Turkey, the Bobwhite Quail, and the Ruffed Grouse are distinct kinds of birds, each with its own physical characteristics and habits. Likewise it is clear to everyone that some species resemble one another much more than others, and may be given group names such as owls, ducks, and swallows. No explanation was long thought necessary beyond the fact that, like the rest of the universe, they were created that way.

The theory of evolution proposed by Darwin in 1859 and soon accepted as correct in its main outlines led to a profound change in our thoughts about such matters. Living things are similar because they have descended over vast periods of time from common ancestors. The fossil Archaeopteryx, a primitive bird still retaining many features of the reptiles from which it evolved, was found in strata that geologists determined to be about 150 million years old.

Some species of birds are more alike than others largely because of the varying lengths of time they have pursued separate evolutionary paths. Let us take three well-known North American species, the Ruby-throated Hummingbird, the Canvasback Duck, and the Wood Duck. If we were able to trace the genealogy of each of these species backward in time generation by generation, we would see the birds gradually change. We might find that 8 million years ago the two ducks split off from a common ancestor but that 50 million years ago the ducks and the Hummingbird had a common ancestor. We can never do this, of course, but in a few groups of animals with better fossil records than birds it is possible to trace some lines of descent in considerable detail.

Darwin called his epoch-making book *The Origin of Species.* The species, he realized, is an all-important and basic unit. Once it could be demonstrated that species change and give rise to new species, other problems of evolution could be tackled with assurance. A century of research by biologists since Darwin has shown that the species is quite as important as it seemed to him and indeed more so. Of all the various categories into which living things are grouped, whether by scientist or layman, the individual and the species are the only ones that have an objective reality in nature. We have already noted that some species are more similar than others and hence—once evolution was recognized as descent with change—more closely related than others.

Beginning with the pre-Darwinian naturalist Linnaeus, biologists have attempted to show these varying degrees of similarity by a definite system. Thus the Mallard and Pintail ducks are very similar and so are placed in the same *genus;* they resemble other ducks, though less closely, so are placed in the *family* Anatidae. This family has some similarities to three species of South American birds called screamers, so the two families, Anatidae and Anhimidae (screamers), are placed together in an *order* Anseriformes. This, along with other orders of birds, is placed in a *class* Aves, which contains all birds and is one of the main constituents of the *subphylum* Vertebrata, or backboned animals.

All these categories as such above the species are mental concepts without reality in nature. We can only define the genus as a group of related species, the family as a group of related genera, and so forth. Just how closely they need to be related or how we shall assess relationships is to a considerable degree a matter of opinion, though we do strive for some consistency. Among the 8600 or so species of birds there are literally hundreds about which experts continue to differ as to which genus, or even family and order they belong to. This is inevitable because, as already noted, these concepts are mere abstractions. The Hooded Merganser is similar to the American Merganser, but is it similar enough to be placed in the same genus? A biologist who tends to see differences rather than similarities might not think so. His opinion is as good as anyone else's.

The species, as already stated, differs from these "higher" categories in that each one is a distinct, concrete entity, just as copper is a different element from chlorine. A species is a population of individuals whose members freely interbreed among themselves and only among themselves. This is a book on distribution, not speciation, so we shall not enter into the various qualifications that hedge this definition. Most of them arise from the fact that species do divide and give rise to daughter species. If copper could be transmuted into chlorine by atomic bombardment, there would be a moment when it was neither one nor the other. Likewise when a species gives rise to two or more daughter species. But since this process of speciation may be long and drawn out, the transition stage can become complicated.

This somewhat lengthy preamble has been necessary for two reasons. In the next chapter we shall attempt to see what can be learned by a consideration of the distribution, past and present, of some of the higher categories—genera, families, and orders—of birds; and it is desirable to understand what such categories are and what they are not. Secondly, and perhaps more important, it turns out that species formation (speciation), one of the basic processes of evolution, takes place, at least in sexually reproducing organisms such as birds and mammals, by a process involving geographical variation in isolation. Since geographical isolation is involved, and usually on a large scale—populations isolated on different mountains, islands, or even continents—it becomes a matter of distribution. It is a matter, moreover, not merely of gross distribution but of the manner in which these isolated populations become adapted to biological and physical environments which are always more or less different. Hence speciation is intimately connected with various basic problems,

ecological and otherwise. Furthermore, as we shall
see, other fascinating problems of "micro-distribution" often arise when formerly isolated populations,
now somewhat changed, meet again as a result of
changes in geology, weather, or mere accidental dispersal.

Let us consider first the methods by which species
of a bird may be broken up into isolated populations.
We have already shown that physical barriers are
effective, even in these flying creatures. This is especially true of sedentary, non-migratory birds. If
such species become scattered on different islands,
mountaintops, or grasslands, either by the chance
effect of storms or by long-term changes in climate
or topography, such populations will be effectively
isolated. Geographical variation, the road to speciation, will begin at once, particularly since no two
isolated environments will be exactly the same.
Sometimes, indeed, a single species occupies very
distinct habitats. The Hermit Thrush, for example,
nests in the hot, sandy Pine Barrens of Long Island,
but elsewhere only in cool mountain forests. Furthermore, the few individuals that found a new colony
of a species will seldom, if ever, represent an exact
cross-section of the population from which they
were drawn. The new population will be in some
degree genetically and hence biologically distinct
from the start.

Complete isolation is not needed for two populations to diverge to species level. In early human his-

tory before there were effective means of transportation, the folk of each island and mountain valley tended to develop a local dialect and customs. If a stranger appeared only rarely, it would not halt this process. But if regular commerce arose between two colonies, the divergence was slowed down. By analogy we may say that two populations of a former species have diverged to the species level when they have reached the point of no longer being able to "communicate" with one another. In birds this may be almost literally true. Distinctions of song and call are among the "isolating mechanisms" that prevent interbreeding between species.

Even in species with a continuous distribution,

Figure 20. Humans, long isolated, have developed different languages; birds, isolated for much longer periods, have evolved into different species.

there may be considerable geographical variation. Experimental work has been carried out on the meadow frog, which is easier to cross in the laboratory than a bird. This frog ranges from New England into Mexico. It has been shown that the terminal populations in New England and in Mexico have become so distinct genetically that they are sterile if crossed. If viewed as an interbreeding geographical unit, this frog is a single species; but if the extremes are compared, it seems to be two species. This Gordian knot would be severed if the range were to be cut at any point. Each segment would become integrated genetically into a separate species, just as surface tension pulls two separated globs of liquid into circular form.

We may use the Great Horned Owl as an example of the sort of variation often found in such partially isolated populations of a species. Those of the northern plains of Canada are nearly as white as a Snowy Owl; those of the cold rain forests of coastal British Columbia almost black; those of Baja California, Mexico, sand-colored and small in size, and so forth. So long as such races are connected and interbreed, speciation does not occur, though the entire species may change in time. Golden Eagles and California Condors, as we know from fossil bones, were of larger size in the Pleistocene, 100,000 years or so ago, than today. This type of "speciation," in which a form changes gradually during geological time, without subdividing, is not to be confused with the or-

dinary use of the term "speciation" to designate the
evolution of new species fostered by geographical
isolation.

When Species Meet

It follows from the above that any widespread
species will have subunits or populations differing
from one another in various ways. This is especially
true of ones that are broken up into various isolated
units on separate pockets of habitat such as islands.
There are literally hundreds of cases among birds,
not to mention other groups, where we find geographical populations so distinct that we do not
know whether they are species or geographical races
(subspecies). A few examples are the Eastern Barred
Owl and the Western Spotted Owl; the American
Red-tailed Hawk and the Eurasian Common Buzzard; the Common Caracara and the extinct Guadalupe Island Caracara. Such units may for conve-
nience be grouped in "superspecies." For example,
the North American Marsh Hawk is a member of a
superspecies with representatives on every continent. Clearly, this concept is of value in the study of
evolution and distribution. Of course, it is sometimes
difficult or impossible to tell whether related allo-
patric (having separate ranges) species or races are
descended from an immediate common ancestor or
whether they are more remotely related. One might
suggest, for example, that the two living species of
elephants—the Indian and the African—form a "su-

perspecies." The fossil record shows that they are by no means that closely related. Unfortunately, fossil evidence for such problems is seldom available for birds.

By this time a paradox has become evident. Although species of birds evolve in geographical isolation, we cannot (usually) tell whether differentiation has reached the species level until the isolation breaks down or is removed! Usually the only way we can tell whether two forms belong to the same species (are "conspecific") is by observing whether they interbreed *in nature*. The fact that they interbreed when crammed together in a cage is no proof, not even if they produce fertile offspring. Some closely related species—for example, the Pintail and the Mallard—do so. Of course if they are sterile when crossed in the laboratory, they are obviously species unless completely connected in nature by interbreeding populations, as in the frog mentioned above.

If two long-isolated populations, derived from a single species, meet, one of two things will happen. Either they will "merge"—that is, interbreed freely —or they will remain separate with no interbreeding or with such sporadic interbreeding, often with partial or complete sterility, that it does not break down or dilute their distinctions. If the first happens, they are still conspecific; if the latter, they have evolved into separate species. When the latter is the case, what happens when the two similar, newly evolved, species come into contact? First, one may extermi-

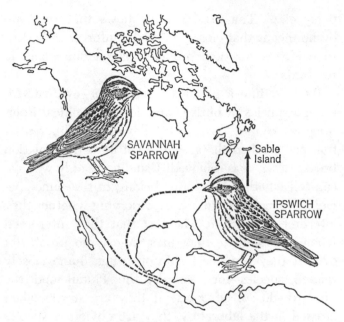

Figure 21. The Savannah Sparrow is found over most of North America, yet it shows little regional variation. When a colony was isolated on tiny Sable Island, however, it evolved into the distinct Ipswich Sparrow.

nate the other. For example, the Ipswich Sparrow of tiny Sable Island, Nova Scotia, is quite clearly a descendant of a colony of Savannah Sparrows. It is now quite different from the mainland Savannah Sparrows from which it descended. If the latter were to colonize Sable Island again, it is possible that they would exterminate the Ipswich Sparrow. This assumes, of course, that the two are now specifically distinct and would not interbreed.

Another possibility is that each of the two daugh-

ter species may be slightly superior in its own habitat. They may then abut along a rather sharp line without overlapping, even in areas that are very similar ecologically. R. K. Selander and D. R. Giller of the University of Texas have analyzed such a case. The eastern Red-bellied Woodpecker and the western Golden-fronted Woodpecker meet in central Texas. They are species; no interbreeding occurs. Neither can penetrate the range of the other. The western species is adapted to drier, the eastern to moister conditions. Although the increase in aridity as one goes west across the Texas Plains is very gradual, given two species that differ as stated, the result will be a sharp line of demarcation. Sometimes, apparently, such similar species may even "repel" each other, so that there is a buffer zone between them occupied by neither one nor the other. Students of distribution should be on the alert for such interesting situations.

Frequently the landscape is not uniform. In such cases the newly adjacent daughter species may be able to overlap but remain ecologically apart, more or less. The Western and Eastern meadowlarks, like the woodpeckers, differ in their tolerance of humidity. They do, however, overlap rather broadly in the Midwest. In such areas the western species favors the drier hillsides, the eastern the moister swales below.

Thus the third possibility, which is foreshadowed by the meadowlarks, is that the two species are sufficiently different at the time they come into contact

to live side by side. The ecologist Gause stated that two species with identical requirements will not be able to exist together in the same environment. Sooner or later, usually sooner, one will eliminate the other as a result of some slight superiority, for example, greater fecundity. This does not mean, of course, that species may not be similar, merely that they must not be identical. Usually it is not difficult to see that similar species differ in their "micro-distribution." Thus one kind of flycatcher may feed chiefly in the treetops, a second in the underbrush, and so forth.

It must be kept in mind that during the initial period of isolation, the ecological differences between such very closely related species develop in separate areas. Although each becomes adapted to local conditions, it does not compete with the other. Once they have come into secondary contact, this is abruptly changed. Competition sets in with the varying results outlined above. This competition will produce a strong natural selection toward making the two less similar and hence less competitive with one another. Most frequently competition will be for

Figure 22. *Bottom*, the Red-bellied Woodpecker (right) in the East and the Golden-fronted Woodpecker (left) in the West are so similar in requirements that they compete where their ranges meet, and no appreciable overlap takes place. *Top*, the ranges of the Cooper's Hawk (bottom) and its smaller cousin the Sharp-shinned Hawk (top) do overlap, but the two never live together in the same woods. After R. Selander.

food. Let us consider an actual case of two related species, the larger Hairy and the smaller Downy woodpeckers. Presumably at the time they first came into contact, the Hairy was a larger bird and fed upon, on the average, larger insects. Selection would then tend to enhance the divergence because intermediate individuals would compete the most. Thus the two species came to divide the environmental resources. Actual studies have shown that the Hairy Woodpecker generally seeks its food on larger branches and trunks than the Downy. The grubs and other insects they secure are, on the average, somewhat different.

As regards groups in which there are considerable numbers of related species living in the same area, one must suppose that this is the result of similar processes continued over a very long time.

Thus far we have discussed very closely allied forms, either subspecies or, at best, species that were once races of a single species. It is often possible to learn a great deal about species, their evolution, their spread, and in some cases their eventual decline and extinction, by studying ones that are not necessarily so closely related. This is especially true on islands, where the total number of species is small and the geographical situation simple. It was not by accident that Darwin first began to think about the origin of species when studying the distribution of the finches of the Galápagos Islands.

Let us, however, consider an example from another archipelago, the Hawaiian Islands. The island of Hawaii, about 4000 square miles in area, has five species of closely related finch-billed honey creepers, three of which are now extinct. Of these, one, *psittacea*, was widespread; a second, *palmeri*, was restricted to scattered areas where there are koa trees; a third, *bailleui*, to scrubby vegetation well up on the big volcanoes. The other two, *flaviceps* and *kona*, became extinct almost immediately; one of them was encountered only in an area of about 12 square miles; the other may have been equally restricted. On the five other islands of the main Hawaiian group, all much smaller in size, ranging in area from 250 to 900 square miles, only one species of this group is found. It is *psittacea*, the most widespread species on the island of Hawaii. It should be noted that the latter island is not only larger than the others, it is also more varied ecologically. From this and other instances one can draw certain conclusions:

Some species are widespread, aggressive, common, and not closely restricted as to habitat. These strong competitors tend to crowd out less aggressive or less well-adapted species, which sometimes can survive by becoming specialized.

The more complex the environment, the more opportunities there are for such survival by specialization. This is the reason, or one of the reasons, for the additional species of finch-billed honey creepers on Hawaii but not on the smaller islands of the group. It is also the reason for the existence of more species of life in a tropical rain forest, the world's richest land environment, than anyplace else.

The interactions of species go on at all levels so that in a genus, whether "advanced" or "primitive," we may find both highly successful and nearly extinct species side by side. Indeed man's closest relatives, the great apes, are at present rather unsuccessful species, despite their high perch in the evolutionary tree. As we know from the fossil record, species that are very abundant at one time may decline to the point of extinction later.

Declining Species

If one compares half a dozen extinct species of Hawaiian birds with an equal number that have survived, there is not always indication of specialization in the former group. Sometimes, indeed, the more bizarre of two species has been the one to persist. One might say that the rare California Condor looks ancient and somehow antediluvian. But as much could be said of some other vultures which are abundant and successful. As pointed out for the Hawaiian species, however, declining species often do have peculiar distributions, probably as a result of the shrinkage of the former range into small pockets of favorable or protected habitat. Colonel Richard Meinertzhagen, an English naturalist, has spoken of certain Tibetan birds as having found refuge on those bleak plateaus "whither their enemies were unable to pursue." Of course, such re-

Figure 23. The California Condor. The decrease in large mammals caused by the Ice Age started a decline in this species that was accelerated by the arrival of the white man in North America.

treat and pursuit is not conscious. Usually it merely involves shrinkage of the former range.

A highly instructive example is provided by the Whooping Crane. The breeding range of this species formerly extended in suitable marshes throughout most of the Great Central Plains of North America, south to Iowa and even Louisiana, and north well into Canada. It wintered to the south, chiefly on the Gulf Coast. Its numbers gradually declined, first because this huge white bird tempted gunners; second because many of the marshes where it nested were drained. By about 1930 there were only twenty or twenty-five of these cranes left in existence. They wintered on the coast of Texas in an area set aside as a refuge and named after the Aransas River. On migration one or two were occasionally seen along the Platte River in Nebraska. But where were they nesting? The late Robert Porter Allen, who was conducting a survey for the National Audubon Society, scoured all the former nesting places but without success, even when aircraft were pressed into service. In 1952 when Allen published his book on these birds he still had not solved this secret. A couple of years later it was found that these few cranes nest in the district of Mackenzie in northern Canada. It is a wilderness not of prairie grass but of low evergreen timber interspersed with vast bogs. Originally this area was probably the least satisfactory part of the nesting range. The weather is so inclement and uncertain that sometimes the handful of remaining pairs do not succeed in rearing a single young. Or perhaps this should be attributed to predation.

The interesting point is this: What was once the "worst" part of the range has now become the "best." Best because it is the only remaining area where these birds can find the security and wilderness they require. In this instance the major portion of the earlier range has become uninhabitable because of human activities. But the ranges of thousands of other species have dwindled or vanished from natural causes—changes in the environment or the evolution and spread of superior competitors.

In recent years some of the marshes in the former

range of the Whooping Crane have been restored. The Lower Souris River Waterfowl Refuge in South Dakota may serve as an example. One might think that the cranes, which see and even visit such areas on their vast annual treks between Canada and Texas, would stop and nest. That they do not do so may be due, if not to learning by the young which follow the parents, then to ingrained habitat preference. We assume that in former days even before the Indian appeared in North America this peripheral part of the population of cranes became adapted for nesting in this far northern, marginal habitat. The rest of the species was extirpated, these birds survived. They may not spread into the former range of the species for centuries. However, if their numbers increased dramatically this would exert population pressure and hasten such a return.

We have pointed out that isolated or semi-isolated populations of a species will always have somewhat different ecologies and hence will acquire local adaptations. There is some reason to believe, as we have just intimated for the crane, that such adaptations may persist indefinitely. The Magpie in the Old World is adapted to a variety of areas—from the humid, verdant British Isles to semi-arid parts of Asia. In North America it is strictly a western species that has never occupied the eastern part of the continent, even though it has been in the hemisphere long enough to give rise to a rather distinct yellow-billed offshoot in California. Presumably the stock that reached North America from Asia was adapted to a "western" ecology and this preference has remained ingrained.

When declining species are migratory their winter as well as breeding range may be unusual. That of the Whooping Crane is peculiar only because of its small size. Perhaps this is because of social bonds between the few remaining individuals, although evidently they migrate separately as families. To turn to other declining species, the Kirtland's Warbler, as noted earlier, nests only in a few counties in the jack-pine belt of Michigan; winters only in the Bahama Islands. The Bristle-thighed

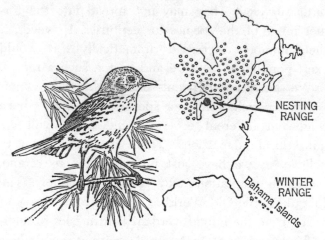

Figure 24. The Jack-pine or Kirtland's Warbler nests only in a small area in Michigan, winters in the Bahamas. The jack-pine tree with which it is associated has a wide range, as shown by the dots, but only in Michigan does it occur in extensive stands that satisfy the needs of this rare bird. After H. Mayfield.

Curlew nests only in dry upland tundra in Alaska where there are few other birds of any sort. It winters only in the mid-Pacific islands, where it was recognized from a specimen collected in Tahiti by one of Captain Cook's expeditions. Not a single individual of this curlew has ever been found in Canada or the United States. Just as relict species often persist on islands because they have less competition there, these relict species of migratory birds enjoy the same security in their insular winter homes.

Rare species of the kinds just mentioned face another threat to their existence. They are much more apt to acquire deleterious hereditary characters than are common birds. If a harmful mutation occurs in a widespread, abundant species, natural selection will eliminate it or keep it at a low level. On the other hand, such a mutation in a species whose total population is very low, such as the Whooping Crane or the California Condor, is apt to spread through the entire population, and perhaps wipe it out. This is due simply to statistical laws of probability. The longer such a population stays at a low numerical ebb, the greater the danger.

This peril also faces many birds whose range is restricted to a single small island. Not only will the population size often be small, but the environment will also be less varied and complex than that available to birds living on continents. This last factor is offset somewhat by the small numbers of species usually found on islands. This allows those that are there to exploit a greater variety of ecological niches than their mainland cousins.

Thus islands are both "good" and "bad" for species. They provide isolation which allows many species to evolve. And since few predators get there, "relicts" and members of declining groups can survive. But isolation cannot be guaranteed forever and islands may be destroyed by further volcanic action or may erode quite away in a comparatively short time, as geological events go. It is not surprising, therefore, that island species—often bizarre and beautiful—sometimes become extinct in a shockingly short time if aggressive competitors are introduced. Or they may be wiped out by introduced disease as may have happened with some of the Hawaiian species. It is for this reason that insular species are seldom able to colonize a larger island or continent. They may reach small islands just off the coast but not get beyond them. Thus the White-crowned Pigeon of the West Indies and Florida Keys has never become established on the mainland.

It thus becomes clear that when, for one reason or another, a species begins to go downhill, it becomes more vulnerable to a number of adverse factors which, cumulatively, may lead to its extinction. Aside from genetic deterioration, it is less well able to cope with disease, predators, and cycles of adverse weather. The Kirtland's Warbler, for example, may be exterminated by the parasitic Cowbird, which has recently increased in the area where this rare warbler nests. The Cowbird lays its eggs in the

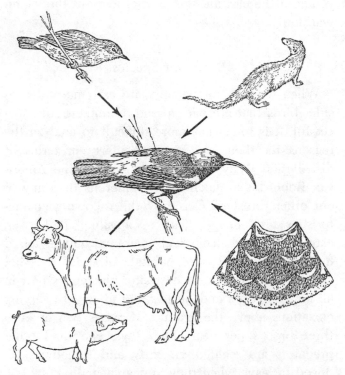

Figure 25. Factors contributing to the extinction of the Mamo of Hawaii (center). Natives used it for feather robes (lower right); the white man introduced enemies such as the mongoose (upper right), competitors such as the Japanese White-eye (upper left), and livestock which exterminated some of the native trees. Perhaps even more serious was avian malaria, carried by birds such as the White-eye and spread by introduced mosquitoes.

nests of the smaller warbler and often the voracious young of the parasite starve or crowd out the young warblers.

Dominant Species

When we turn to the opposite extreme and consider birds that are widespread, abundant, and successful, it is somewhat more difficult to analyze the reasons for their success, particularly in terms of distribution. Why, for example, should the American Robin be so much more numerous than any of our other thrushes? Certainly the following characteristics are among those responsible: It has an extremely broad ecological tolerance and is found in almost every type of habitat. Likewise it is not at all particular as to a nest site, placing its nest in all kinds of trees and bushes and at widely varying elevations above the ground. It raises two or even three broods per year. Blue Jays, cats, and other predators are scolded violently and sometimes induced to leave when they appear near its nest. If a cowbird succeeds in laying one of its eggs in a robin's nest, the latter promptly pushes it out. The food is varied and it can switch from earthworms in spring to withered berries in winter. Thus the Robin, and the same would be true in varying degrees of all widespread, numerous species, has acquired characteristics that assure its success unless there is some drastic change in the environment. Heavy spraying of elms with DDT has caused such a change locally in the Midwest. Earthworms accumulate the chemical and the Robins are killed. But, again, it is such a widespread and numerous species that the effects are only local.

Such dominant species have an inhibiting competitive effect upon related species which is often difficult to detect without detailed study of local distribution and ecology. Mr. Otto Horvath of the University of British Columbia has found that in parts of that province the Varied Thrush is to some extent limited in its choice of nesting areas to ones not pre-empted by the Robin.

Perhaps the characteristics of dominant species can be better understood by considering those whose range is expanding; at any rate, the distributional aspects are more obvious. This is to some extent true of the Robin, but there are more spectacular examples.

The continental sweep of the House Sparrow and the Starling after their introduction in New York by man is well known. Both, especially the Starling, have had a deleterious effect on some of our native birds such as the Bluebird and Meadowlark. Wild species sometimes show similar expansions. A recent example is the Turkish Turtle Dove which in a decade or two has spread from the Middle East over much of Europe. Some changes of this kind are probably correlated with long-term climatic trends, others do not seem to be.

The recent "population explosion" of the Cattle Egret may be cited as a final and unusual example.

This Old World species first appeared in South America about thirty years ago, perhaps earlier. Whether it was blown across the Atlantic (as one or two individuals of other herons banded in Spain have been) or whether it escaped from a zoo is not known. For a time it did nothing. Then suddenly it began to spread. Within fifteen or twenty years it appeared throughout the West Indies and southern North America. It now occurs in Florida by the thousands, nests as far north as New Jersey and even Canada.

Though this might be attributed solely to the spread of a species on a new continent, there is some indication that something happened to the species at about the time this tremendous expansion began. Even in Africa where it is native it spread to areas of the southern part of that continent where it previously had been rare or unknown. It also appeared and is spreading rapidly in Australia, especially in the north where the water buffalo, introduced for rice culture, has gone wild. It is possible, however, that the population of that continent stems from an introduction by man.

It does not, of course, get us very far to suggest that in such a case some genetical change in the species, either a chance recombination of the genes or the end result of a gradual adaptive change, suddenly permitted the species to expand in numbers, in range, or in both. On the other hand, there is nothing genetically impossible or even improbable about the occasional occurrence of such an event.

In summary, during the long course of evolution the distribution and numbers of all species have changed, sometimes gradually, sometimes suddenly. Thousands have become extinct, others have become so transformed as to be, in effect, new species. Still other thousands of new species have evolved in geographical isolation. These processes are so prolonged as to be barely perceptible without examination of a fossil record. Nevertheless, patient study of the range and numerical status of living species provides many clues to the history of evolution and to its mechanics. Furthermore, the violent changes man is imposing upon nature are, in some cases, affecting the distribution of birds in somewhat the same way as did geological or climatic episodes in the past. For all these reasons, it is important to regard distribution not as a thing isolated and static, but as a phenomenon intimately related to the long and varied course of evolution.

Chapter 6

DISTRIBUTION OF HIGHER
SYSTEMATIC CATEGORIES

A complete presentation of the distribution of the higher categories of birds, still less of the species and genera, is beyond the scope of this book. Rather we shall discuss briefly some of the orders. These have been selected to illustrate problems encountered in such studies and the kind of conclusions that may be drawn from them. At the end of the chapter an analysis of a single family, the Corvidae or crow family, is given and in this case the discussion is carried down to the level of genera.

Conclusions based upon the distribution of systematic groups can be only as sound as the classification upon which they are based. For example, the New World vultures Cathartidae are so distinct anatomically that some consider them unrelated to the other birds of prey and would set up an order for them. The Old World vultures, on the other hand, are definitely offshoots of the typical birds of prey; they are, to stretch a point, "degenerate eagles." This seems like a very nice instance of a group, the New World vultures, evolving to fill an empty ecological niche. It comes as a surprise, therefore, to learn that there were numerous Old World vultures in North America until very recently. Their bones are mingled with those of New World vultures in the Ice Age tar pits of California. Furthermore, there were New World vultures in Europe (and presumably elsewhere in the Old

World) although they disappeared some millions of
years ago. These facts put an entirely different slant
on our ideas about these groups. Obviously, however, we must be sure of our facts. Are the European
fossils assigned to the Cathartidae—evidently confined to a few, sometimes fragmentary, leg and foot
bones—indubitably members of this family? Again,
might not the North American Old World vultures
actually have evolved from North American ancestors? Even if this were the case, to be sure, it would
not explain why they all became extinct whereas
some of the cathartid vultures did not.

If such doubts are pushed too far we may find
ourselves reasoning in a circle. Instead of stating
the distribution of a group, we decide what can
belong to a group by considering its distribution.
This can lead to errors.

Even when the facts are not in question, differences of opinion may lead to difficulty. For example, the breeding range of the Towhee is eastern
North America. If, however, we consider it conspecific with the western Spurred Towhee, the range
becomes continent-wide. In such cases it will usually be clear what is meant.

The problems also exist at higher levels of classification. For example, we may agree that tropic-
birds are related to pelicans but disagree as to
whether the relationship is close enough to war-
rant placing them in the same order. Such problems, which often affect the distribution of a group,
are based on the fact, emphasized in the previous

chapter, that systematic categories, other than the species, are to a degree abstractions. And even the species, as just noted in the case of the Towhees, gives quite as many difficulties, simply because, in many instances, we have no method of establishing whether or not a particular form is in fact a species, or only a race.

GIANT FLIGHTLESS BIRDS—RATITES

This group includes the Ostrich of Africa, the South American Ostrich, or Rhea, and its relatives the tinamous; the emus and cassowaries of Australia and New Guinea; the Kiwi; the fossil moas of New Zealand; and the fossil Elephant-bird, which weighed up to 1000 pounds, of Madagascar. How closely all these groups are related and how many orders they represent are still moot questions. No ratites living or fossil are known from North America. On the other hand, ostriches roamed across Asia until the Pleistocene.

The distribution of the ratites, all of which with the exception of the tinamous are flightless, poses one of the most difficult problems in avian zoogeography. We know from numerous other examples that island species, presumably because of an absence of competitors and predators, often attain giant size and, in the case of birds, lose the power of flight. It is certain that these ratites are descended from flying birds and do not represent a direct flightless lineage going back to the reptiles. In the case of the species found on islands—Madagascar,

New Zealand, and even Australia—it is reasonable to conclude that their ancestors reached these islands before losing the power of flight. The ostrich, because of its tremendous speed and alertness, survives even in predator-infested Africa but in general there are fewer big flightless birds on the various continents now than in an earlier era when predatory mammals were less highly evolved. In a world dominated by mammals they are something of an anachronism.

PENGUINS
ORDER SPHENISCIFORMES

The penguins are the best example of a group restricted to the Antarctic and Subantarctic. One or two of them have followed the cold currents of western South America north as far as Peru and the Galápagos Islands, but none has ever crossed the tropics and reached the Arctic.

PETRELS, ALBATROSSES, AND SHEARWATERS
ORDER PROCELLARIIFORMES

These are the most typically marine of all birds, coming to land only to nest, and unlike penguins not even deigning to rest on an ice cake. Of this order, the albatrosses and diving petrels are restricted almost entirely to the southern oceans, though three species of albatross do nest on islands of the north-central Pacific. Of the fifty odd species of shearwaters and fulmars, there are only a few northern and tropical representatives. The storm petrels are equally widespread, found throughout the oceans of the world.

PELICANS
ORDER PELECANIFORMES

This aquatic order, which includes the pelican and its relatives, is found throughout the world, chiefly in the tropical and temperate belts. The tropic-birds, as the name would suggest, and the frigate-birds are restricted to tropical seas. The pelicans, and the boobies and gannets, occur in cooler latitudes as well as in the tropics. Cormorants are the most widespread of the order. Some of the species live in such inclement regions as the Aleutian Islands and around Cape Horn.

LOONS
ORDER GAVIIFORMES

An example of a small group of only four or five species restricted entirely to the northern hemisphere. All of the species are found at one season or another in both North America and Eurasia. Northern United States and Scotland are the southern nesting limits for the loons.

SHORE BIRDS
ORDER CHARADRIIFORMES

In the shore birds, the largest family, that of the sandpipers, is remarkable for the number of species nesting in the Arctic or the Subarctic—the Knot and the Sanderling, to name only two. Of the family, only a few snipe and woodcock live in the southern hemisphere. The plovers are more widespread, as are some of the specialized shore birds such as oyster-catchers and avocets; the Crab Plover, however, is restricted to the Indian Ocean area.

The second main suborder comprises the terns, gulls, and skuas. While terns are cosmopolitan, the gulls and skuas are chiefly northern but with some southern hemisphere species. The third suborder, the auks, is a typical northern group of birds—the northern ecological counterpart of the penguins and diving petrels, though one or two species nest as far south as the Gulf of California. In the East none nests farther south than Maine, but bones of the extinct Great Auk have been found in Florida, showing that it was driven that far south during the Glacial Age.

WATERFOWL
ORDER ANSERIFORMES

The hundred-odd species of ducks, geese, and swans are an ancient and cosmopolitan group. Often powerful awing and highly migratory, several genera are extremely far-flung. On the other hand, some of the most striking genera—especially in the tropics—are far more restricted. Australia and New Zealand have several aberrant types such as the Musk Duck, the Pink-eared Duck, and the Cape Barren Goose. Fossils indicate that the last named once had relatives in New Zealand and even Hawaii.

STORKS
ORDER CICONIIFORMES

This order, comprised of herons, storks, ibises, and spoonbills, is chiefly a fresh-water group. It is represented throughout the world in marshes and along shores. Several of the species such as the Glossy Ibis and the Great Egret are almost cosmopolitan. As with the preceding order, one finds some peculiar forms of restricted distribution such as the Boat-billed Heron in South America, and the Shoebill and Hammerhead storks in Africa.

FLAMINGOS
ORDER PHOENICOPTERIFORMES

An ancient lineage, the flamingos inhabit the lagoons and shallow lakes of the West Indies, Yucatan, perhaps formerly southern Florida, South America, Africa, southern Europe, and southwest Asia to India. Though absent from Australia, three fossil species have recently been described from there. Apparently the post-Pleistocene desiccation that converted Australia into the "Dry Continent" eliminated the flamingos, along with much else. Some think the flamingos are allied to storks (Ciconiiformes), others to waterfowl (Anseriformes); others point to their long fossil history as evidence that they are probably not close to any order. So far as distribution is concerned, it is too early to theorize as to the point of origin of this order.

CRANES
ORDER GRUIFORMES

Though scarcely water birds, the more common members of the order such as rails and cranes are partial to marshes. The order shows every evidence of being an ancient one. A few widespread and more or less flourishing families include the cranes, rails, bustards, and button quail. Then there is a cluster of small families at least two of which may be geographical relicts—the Kagu of New Caledonia and the three species of mesites of Madagascar. The main tide of evolution has probably swept by additional small families of the Gruiformes such as the plains wanderers of Australia (one species), the sun grebes (one species in the Orient, one in South America), the cariamas (two species in southern South America), and the sun bitterns (one species, tropical America). The cariamas are apparently related to a large assemblage of fossil species of the western hemisphere known as phorhorhacids. These were long-legged, heavy-beaked ground birds, probably of somewhat predatory habits. Hence they were not unlike the living Secretary-bird of Africa to which they were possibly related.

PHEASANTS
ORDER GALLIFORMES

The fowl-like birds are a large and ancient order. Of rather weak power of flight, the families tend to be somewhat circumscribed geographically. Only the quail are cosmopolitan. Grouse extend around the northern hemisphere. The turkeys may be an early American offshoot of the splendid oriental pheasants, while the discovery of the Congo Peacock as recently as 1936 shows that this group reached Africa also. South America is the home of the specialized and presumably primitive Hoatzin, whose young climb about the mangroves with their wing claws, as described so dramatically by William Beebe, and also of the curassows, which may represent the ancestral stock of the entire order.

Australia is the home of the unique megapodes, or incubator-birds, whose eggs, buried in warm sand and rotting vegetation, hatch without incubation. The ancestors of the incubator-birds surely brooded their eggs like other birds; the egg-burying habit is not a trait held over directly from the reptiles. This family shows some island-hopping ability. One species has reached the tiny Palau Islands in the Pacific. One or two others have spread slightly beyond the Australian area to the Philippines and Celebes.

HAWKS
ORDER FALCONIFORMES AND
OWLS
ORDER STRIGIFORMES

Birds of prey are powerful fliers and many of them are very widespread. Kestrels, peregrine falcons, buteos, accipters, and fish hawks similar to those of the United States are found nearly or almost nearly around the world. The same species of Barn Owl nests in the United States, Europe, India, Africa,

Australia, and the Fiji Islands. The American vultures on the other hand, are strictly a western hemisphere group, at least at present. The Andean and California Condors, the latter now almost extinct, are the largest flying birds today (rivaled only by the biggest albatrosses). Even larger Condors flew about in the Pleistocene scavenging upon the vast assemblage of mammoths, giant ground sloths, and other beasts that roamed the continent at that time. The Ice Age spelled demise for most of them—giant mammals and giant vultures.

PARROTS
ORDER PSITTACIFORMES

The American tropics and the Australian region —all the way out to Fiji and Tahiti—have a great variety and abundance of parrots. In Africa and India there are few. Why this is so is an unanswered question.

The parrots are by and large a tropical or subtropical group. Even the extinct Carolina Parakeet had its stronghold in the Florida Everglades, an outpost of the subtropics. This does not mean that one must conjure up land bridges to account for the presence of parrots throughout the world. Even today, the Kea parrot nests in the snowy New Zealand Alps in mid-winter, thus proving that we cannot assume that all parrots are, or were in the past, tropical. It only needed one or two such hardy forms to spread across the former land bridge connecting Alaska with Siberia. The climate is known to have been much warmer in the Tertiary, some millions of years ago. Yet the parrots of the New and Old World have been separated so long that they represent distinct branches of the family. In this they might be comparable, for example, with the New and Old World monkeys.

HUMMINGBIRDS AND SWIFTS
ORDER APODIFORMES

One of the commonest questions asked of the ornithologist is, "Why are there no hummingbirds in Europe or Africa?" The answer, which to a layman may seem non-responsive, is simply, "Because they evolved in the tropics of the Americas and have not spread farther than the New World." The family is a classic example of one restricted by physical barriers rather than by ecology. At least it seems to us that hummingbirds would do as well in the tropics throughout the world.

How long has it taken three hundred species of diversified hummers to evolve in South America? The Andes, whose many ranges have provided much of the local isolation for speciation, were thrown up in mid-Tertiary, perhaps 25 million years ago. Purely as a guess, a minimum of 20 million years may have been required.

PERCHING BIRDS
ORDER PASSERIFORMES

About two-thirds of the 8600 species of living birds belong to this great order. They are the most

numerous, and presumably the most advanced, of
birds. On the average, they are smaller in size than
non-passerine birds, with the exception of a few
aberrant groups of the latter such as the hummingbirds. This sort of prevalence or numerical dominance of a single group is common in evolution.
Beetles are an example among the insects, the ro-
dents among mammals, and the Compositae, or
daisy family, among plants. It is believed that the
great "flowering" of the Passeriformes accompanied
the evolution of the flowering plants into botanical
dominance during the Tertiary period. Some of the
largest and most successful families of songbirds
feed on the seeds and nectar of these plants. Others
live upon the insects which evolved in great profusion and feed upon the flowering plants.

It should be added that the perching birds, though
so successful and numerous, are unable to compete
with many types of larger birds of more ancient
lineage—especially water birds. And of course some
predatory birds—owls and hawks—find in the small
perching birds not competition but merely an additional food supply.

Even within the order Passeriformes there has
been both success and relative failure. One group,
the true songbirds or Oscines, contains about two-
thirds of the species. It is significant that all or most
of the seed- and nectar-eating types belong to this
subgroup—to be sure, along with some insect-eating
groups such as the warblers and wrens.

The possession of a slightly less elaborate voice

box, or syrinx, can scarcely be advanced seriously as a reason for a major group doing less well in the world. Nevertheless, it does characterize the second major (but less numerous) subgroup of the perching birds which were formerly designated Clamatores because they "clamor" rather than carol. And it is true that the families of the Clamatores, aside from the smaller number of species, do show some distributional evidence of being a declining group. Consider, for example, the following:

Lyrebirds—Only two species, restricted to Australia.

Australian scrub wrens—Australia only; two species both with small ranges.

New Zealand wrens—New Zealand only; four species.

Philepittas—Madagascar only; four species.

Broadbills—Tropical Asia and Africa; there are only two African species and one of these is localized in the Kivu Mountains.

Pittas—The Asiatic species are in many cases restricted to the East Indies, suggesting a sheltering insular effect. Six species in Africa and Australia.

The remaining Clamatores, about five families, are chiefly South American. Here, there are several hundred species in all. South America, however, is something of a refuge itself. Most of the principal groups of true songbirds, or Oscines, are of Old World origin and some of them either have not reached the western hemisphere at all, or if they have, are chiefly North American. Thus less pressure has been put on the Clamatores in the New World than in the Old World tropics.

For the songbirds, or Oscines, it is possible to give only the briefest summary of distribution. There is a core of Old World families which, because of their rather large-size, relatively long outer wing quill and generalized feeding habits, among other things, seems primitive. Here belong such families as the crows, starlings, shrikes, bowerbirds, birds of paradise, drongos, Old World orioles, and a few others. Of these only the crow family has reached the New World, chiefly North America, in any numbers. A second main group of songbirds which includes the thrushes, bulbuls, babblers, Old World warblers and flycatchers, and others, is also better represented in the Old than in the New World. Australia and New Guinea share in this abundance. What representatives there are in the New World, such as thrashers, thrushes, and wrens, are often better represented in North than in South America. The genus *Turdus* among the thrushes, however, is nearly cosmopolitan and is well represented in South America.

Passing now to the more advanced and specialized songbirds, one Old World group, modified for nectar eating, includes the sunbirds, flowerpeckers, white-eyes, and perhaps the Australian honey eaters. Another large and important group contains the New World orioles, the wood warblers, the honey creepers, the tanagers, and a variety of finches and buntings. Indeed the seed-eating finches, considered from the broadest point of view, seem to represent the apex of the evolutionary tree of birds. They are to be found in greater or lesser profusion in every quarter of the globe.

The Crow Family

As an example of distributional analysis applied to a family we have selected the Corvidae, or crow family.

The jays are usually considered the most primitive members of the family and the most like the majority of songbirds. Two genera, *Platylophus* and *Platysmurus*, of the Oriental Region may be very primitive jays. They resemble in some ways such primitive songbirds as the helmet shrikes and seem to indicate that the Corvidae may have evolved from such stock in the Old World. The typical jays are found both in the Old and New worlds. They are commoner in the New World where one genus, *Cyanocorax*, with several species, extends throughout most of South America. It is the only genus of Corvidae to have reached that continent. Another genus of jays, *Perisoreus*, is found around the northern hemisphere, one of the many genera in various families to do so in the far north. This genus has a localized species in the mountains of western China.

As noted above, the jays are thought to have evolved in the Old World. The reason there are fewer of them there is probably that they have been partially replaced by or have evolved into more advanced groups of corvids. One of these is the magpies. Actually certain long-tailed jays of Mexico are all but magpies. In the Old World the transition is shown by a very handsome, somewhat specialized jay of the Ryukyu Islands south of Japan.

Magpies are numerous in the Orient and India but only two genera occur in temperate Eurasia. One of them, the Azure-winged Magpie, has a very curious disconnected distribution. It is found in Spain and then again in Japan and the Far East. We assume it was once found in the vast intervening area, for one can scarcely expect it to have been carried that far by a storm! The other genus, containing the common Pie, or "Mag" Pie as it was nicknamed in England at an early day, has reached western North America from Alaska to California. In Africa there are two magpies, both very peculiar and of dubious affinities within the family.

The jays have given rise to other lines of corvine evolution besides the magpies. In Tibet one finds several species of curious ground-living jays. The most specialized of them, *Pseudopodoces,* is as small as a sparrow and as dully colored. The nutcrackers, one species in Eurasia, one in the Rocky Mountains, are also offshoots of the jays. So for that matter are the crows and ravens of the genus *Corvus.*

The latter genus contains the ravens, the largest of all "songbirds," even though they do not sing. As is well known, crows and ravens are very adaptable, perhaps the best endowed mentally of all birds. Konrad Lorenz, the distinguished authority on animal behavior, has found evidence that leads him to believe that a raven, and only that species, may utter a sound or word that may sometimes have a symbolic meaning, as in our own words.

Be that as it may, the genus *Corvus* is a fine example of a very successful group of species that has spread far and wide. Though unspecialized, they are not, in some ways, typical songbirds. In Australia, New Guinea, Madagascar, most of Africa, the West Indies, and Hawaii, crows and ravens are the *only* representatives of the family. Only in South America are they somewhat surprisingly absent.

In the previous chapter we found that an analysis of the distribution of species tells us much about their evolution and sometimes their subsequent decline. In this chapter we have tried to show that a similar consideration of higher categories is not merely informative but actually vital to a comprehension of the long sweep of evolution.

Chapter 7

GEOGRAPHICAL PATTERNS
OF DISTRIBUTION—
FAUNAS

In the last chapter we considered the distribution of various orders, families, genera, and species of birds. The one family discussed in any detail, the Corvidae, or crow family, was found to be cosmopolitan. Many families are not so widespread. If we plot the distribution of all the families and orders of birds as well as those of other animals, and plants on a world map, certain patterns become apparent. One notices a few major biogeographic regions,

Figure 26. The classical biogeographical regions of the world are shown on this polar projection.

each characterized by a certain number of families found nowhere else—that is, families endemic to a particular region. They are as follows, with a list of some of the endemic groups of birds characteristic of each.

Nearctic Region: North America, except the tropical portions of Mexico and Central America.

Turkeys. Evidently a Nearctic family or subfamily, though one of the two living species is tropical Mexican.

Wren Tit. This Pacific Coast species is often placed in a separate family, but it may be a member of the Old World babbler family.

Also many endemic genera, such as the Plains Grouse (Sage Hen, Prairie Chicken) and various blackbirds and finches.

Palearctic Region: The temperate portions of Eurasia and North Africa. In Asia the Himalaya Mountains separate the Palearctic Region to the north from the Oriental Region to the south.

The only endemic family is the hedge sparrows. As in the Nearctic Region, there are a considerable number of endemic genera.

Ethiopian Region: Africa, south of the Sahara, and Madagascar.

Among the endemic families are the ostriches, shoebill storks, hammerhead storks, secretary-birds, dodos (Mauritius and nearby islands), mesites (Madagascar), turacos, mousebirds, philepittas

(Madagascar), helmet shrikes and vanga shrikes (Madagascar).

A few of these groups, the ostriches, the mousebirds, and possibly the turacos, constitute separate orders.

Oriental or Indian Region: Tropical Asia: India, Ceylon, southeastern Asia, Philippine Islands, and East Indies, east to but not including the Spice Islands (Moluccas).

The fairy bluebirds seem to be the only endemic family and even they may be a subfamily of the bulbuls. There are many very distinct genera among such families as the pheasants, hornbills, and others.

Australian Region: Australia, Tasmania, Spice Islands, New Guinea, and all the smaller islands to the north and east, including New Caledonia and Oceania, out to and including Tahiti and Hawaii.

Among the endemic families are the emus, cassowaries, kiwis (New Zealand), kagus (New Caledonia), plains wanderers, incubator-birds (one reaching the Philippines), lyrebirds, scrub-birds, New Zealand wrens (New Zealand), wattled crows (New Zealand), birds of paradise, bowerbirds, bell magpies, honey eaters and Hawaiian honey creepers (Hawaii).

Neotropical Region: South America, tropical parts of North America, north to southern Mexico and even the southern tip of Florida; West Indies.

Among the approximately thirty endemic families, several of ordinal rank, are the following: rheas, tinamous, screamers, cariamas, trumpeters, hoatzins, toucans, todies (West Indies), jacamars, motmots, puffbirds, ant-birds, ovenbirds, cotingas, manakins, and plant cutters.

Marine Region: Oceans of the world.

Penguins, petrels (several families), boobies, frigate-birds, tropic-birds, and sheathbills are the more important families of marine birds. Many genera and species of certain other families such as terns and cormorants also belong in this group. A very few birds such as the phalaropes (three species) and jaegers (four species) behave as land birds when nesting, but winter at sea.

Let us now proceed to analyze these biogeographic regions from several points of view.

Barriers

In an early chapter we pointed out that if the world were uniform throughout in climate and lacked such barriers as mountains or oceans, every bird species would be distributed over the entire globe. Instead, as we can see from the above, many families and even some orders, not to mention species, are restricted to one or another area. Obviously this has been the result of barriers to dispersal, both past and present, which have permitted evolution to go on in isolation. The large number of endemic families in the two most isolated continents—South America and Australia—demonstrates this.

In some cases the break between regions is sharper than would be expected. The most famous example is "Wallace's Line," passing between the adjacent Lesser Sunda and Spice Islands off New Guinea and separating the Oriental and Australian regions. The break is far more definite than one would anticipate from the present geography.

The break between the Neotropical and Nearctic regions in Mexico is fairly sharp. On the other hand, the birds of the colder regions of Patagonia in Argentina and the Falkland Islands off the tip of South America clearly belong to the neotropical fauna. In this case the presence in North America of various groups of birds, many of Eurasian origin, may inhibit the northward spread of neotropical types, which, nevertheless, has been considerable in such families as the tyrant flycatchers.

In other words the biogeographic regions are a result of long isolation. They tend to coincide with the major continents. The separation between tropics and non-tropics has, though fluctuating, been almost as ancient, so that one finds that in Mexico, in Asia, and in Africa, the borders between regions coincide more or less with the limits of the tropics.

Comparing the Regions

A glance at the above list will show that the biogeographic regions differ enormously in rank, as measured by numbers of endemic bird families. The Nearctic, Palearctic, and Oriental regions can scarcely muster one endemic family each. Evaluated strictly on this basis, Madagascar and New Zealand are better defined. Obviously we tend to be influenced by the size of such areas as North America. If the Nearctic and the Palearctic are regarded not as separate regions but as subregions of a single "Holarctic" Region, the situation is much improved. This region has, then, several endemic families such as the loons, phalaropes, auks, and grouse.

As one proceeds south in North America, the percentage of birds originating in the Neotropical Region increases. In Eurasia the same is true of Ethiopian and Oriental forms. This is especially the case in the Far East where, in the absence of the Himalayan barrier, various otherwise tropical forms extend north to Japan or Manchuria.

As regards the Oriental Region, it must first be said that it is better characterized by mammals than by birds. Secondly, it has a very strong tie with the Ethiopian Region including, in the case of birds, Madagascar. The extreme desiccation of the Middle East is very recent. Before that Africa and tropical Asia enjoyed a much closer faunal connection. Even among mammals, which by no means equal birds in dispersal ability, a number of species are found even today in both India and Africa—lion, spotted hyena, leopard, cheetah, and so forth. The Oriental and Ethiopian regions are too distinct, however, to join into a single region. Yet if this were done, a number of families would be entirely or nearly endemic to this area. Examples are the hornbills, broadbills, pittas, sunbirds, crab plovers, honey guides, and others.

It must be emphasized that there is considerable overlap, so far as birds are concerned, among all the regions. The Corvidae is by no means the only family of birds that is cosmopolitan. In the Australian Region, as an example of such overlap between regions, one finds the following Oriental or at least Old World families represented by a single or at most by two or three species: bustards, rollers, hornbills, drongos, sunbirds, and bee eaters, among others. From an ecological point of view several of these species are abundant and important in Australia even though all presumably are newcomers to the region. From the faunal, or biogeographical, point of view, on the other hand, one is interested in the center of the present distribution of an order or family as indicated by the number of genera or species (but not individuals!) found there. For example, the larks are predominantly an Old World group. Yet the Horned Lark, the only species to reach North America, has spread abundantly over most of that continent and even has established a race in Colombia, South America. Nevertheless it is not even specifically distinct from the Horned Lark of Asia. The biogeographer will be more impressed by the fact that there are many genera and dozens of species of larks in the Palearctic and Ethiopian regions.

The Regions and Past Distribution

The author of the most recent treatise on the zoogeography of the vertebrates, Professor P. J. Darlington, emphasizes that biogeographic regions must be based upon species now living in the areas in question. This may be true but inasmuch as the present limits of families often reflect conditions going back for millions of years, it is necessary to keep this fact in mind! It is impressive to learn that the Ostrich constitutes a family and even an order endemic to the Ethiopian Region. This becomes less significant when we learn that as recently as the Pleistocene a few thousand years ago, ostriches occurred in the Palearctic as far away as China! They may even have evolved in the Palearctic.

With a few possible exceptions, such as the penguins, there are no orders or families of birds with a complete enough fossil record to enable us to be sure where they evolved. The probabilities are sometimes high enough, of course. Thus one would consider it most unlikely that the lyrebirds evolved elsewhere than in Australia.

What role then, do fossils play in the study of the biogeographic regions? They can, first of all, show us how different things were in the past. Obviously Bavaria was not the same 150 million years ago in the Jurassic when Archaeopteryx was flapping about in what was then tropical forests. Indeed, the study of fossils can give an entirely different impression of the zoogeographic regions.

We have seen that on the basis of endemic families of birds, the Nearctic scarcely qualifies as a major region. It is, to exaggerate somewhat, a "melting pot" between Old World elements that arrived via Siberia and neotropical elements that originated in South America and became progressively more important as one proceeds southward.

But let us take a glimpse at the past bird life of North America. In the Cretaceous, about 100 million years ago, a remarkably specialized, somewhat loonlike diving bird called *Hesperornis* occurred; also an

Figure 27. The loonlike, toothed Hesperornis (bottom) lived in shallow inland seas in Kansas during the Cretaceous; the huge, clumsy Diatryma (top) roamed Wyoming in the Eocene.

early flying bird, *Ichthyornis*. In the Eocene, perhaps 70 million years ago, North America was the home of the giant, huge-billed *Diatryma*. This may or may not have been near the ancestral line of the chiefly South American phorhorhacids, of which a giant species that inhabited Florida during the Pleistocene (that is to say within the past million years or less) has recently been named.

The New World vultures, presumably a North American group, had a long-legged terrestrial form, *Neocathartes,* during the Eocene in Montana. It was quite unlike the later members of the group, which are big-winged, soaring scavengers. Of the latter certain giant forms, the teratorns, which became extinct in the Pleistocene, are considered distinct enough to form a separate family. As a final example of a striking fossil form described from North America we may mention a huge sea bird, known from our Pacific Coast. Called *Osteodontornis* because its beak had a plentiful supply of pseudo-teeth for holding fish, it is estimated to have had a wingspread of 17 feet. This means it may have had the greatest span of any bird ever.

The fact that all these and other remarkable birds inhabited North America in the past, does not, of course, mean that they all evolved there or were restricted to that continent, though certainly some of them were. The point to be stressed is that the biogeographic regions of, say, 25 million years ago were doubtless very different in rank and, in some cases at least, in geographical limits from those of today. North America was surely more important; Australia, on the other hand, may have been less so. Doubtless these differences were due to the fact that the climate during many of these epochs was tropical or subtropical over large parts of the world.

W. D. Matthew, a great paleontologist, for many years with The American Museum of Natural History, concluded that the temperate regions of the northern hemisphere were the cradle of evolution and that the major groups of animals evolved there and migrated into the southern hemisphere. On the other hand, Darlington, primarily a student of living forms, concluded that the tropics were the center of evolution. It is probably true that more groups have evolved in tropical areas than elsewhere, but it is also true, as we have just seen, that at various times in the past most parts of the world enjoyed a tropical climate.

Lesser Faunal Units

The major biogeographic regions, as we have seen, are characterized not merely by numerous endemic species and genera, but even by families and orders. Some islands are also very distinct, Madagascar and New Zealand being the best examples. Each has been considered a region by some authorities and at the very least is to be given the rank of a subregion. Some other islands also have very distinct avifaunas.

Thus almost all the land birds of Hawaii and of the Galápagos are distinct at the species level, and each of these island groups has one distinct family or subfamily of birds. New Caledonia has a bird, the Kagu, that belongs to an endemic family, and several unique species. Celebes has several very peculiar genera.

There are a number of reasons why biologists hesitate to regard such islands as full-fledged "regions." The total number of birds is small. If one is considering other groups as well, land mammals are usually few or wanting and land reptiles may be absent also. Finally, despite its distinctness the fauna of such islands is often very clearly allied to that of one of the larger regions. For example, the birds of New Zealand, as a whole, are definitely related to those of Australia.

Islands that are close to continents or which were formerly parts of continents have less distinct faunas. But big varied tropical islands such as Sumatra or Borneo always have a good many endemic races, species, genera, and occasionally even families of birds. In the temperate and arctic regions, on the other hand, where the bird life is less rich and where many of the species are migratory (and hence more apt to mix with continental forms), island faunas are much less distinct. Thus the British Isles have no endemic families or genera, and but one endemic species, the Red Grouse. Then there are a few British subspecies, most of them not very distinct.

As measured not by what is present but by what is absent, the avifaunas of many islands are more peculiar. Numbers of widespread continental species are usually absent. Such "depauperate" faunas are, as just noted, characteristic of islands and are the result of two factors. First, certain species never get across the water gap to the island; second, some that do so are unable to become established. Islands are less varied than the mainland and some of the habitats, even if present, are too restricted for certain species of birds. Nevertheless, even small, poorly isolated and recent islands such as Cape Sable Island, Nova Scotia, may have distinct and interesting forms, in this case the Ipswich Sparrow. Though some species cannot become established on islands, others hold out there long after they have disappeared on the mainland.

Within large continental areas one finds faunal areas, or "centers of differentiation," by plotting the ranges of subspecies, species, and, less often, genera and families. Often these are rather poorly marked because only a small percentage of the birds fit the pattern. Furthermore, such faunal areas often coincide with and are obviously partly or even entirely the result of existing ecological conditions. For example, the forested area of southwestern Australia, sharply delineated on all sides by desert or ocean, has as would be expected quite a different avifauna from the surrounding brush or desert regions. Nevertheless, when such an area has a certain number of species or other forms that are not found elsewhere, it must be regarded as a separate fauna.

A recent attempt to divide the Nearctic Region into avian faunal areas has been made by Professor Miklos Udvardy of the University of British Columbia. Considering only the perching birds, he divided the region into seventeen faunas. Some of these are further divided into twenty-five subfaunas. Even so, some thirty chiefly widespread species are not included. This latter number would have been far greater if the non-passerine birds such as hawks, shore birds, and ducks had been included, for many of them are very wide-ranging.

Without discounting the value of this analysis, consideration of the "indicator" species of some of Udvardy's faunas will show that these areas are somewhat indefinite rather than clear-cut. For example, his Arctic Fauna has three subdivisions one of which is the "subarctic tundra-forest." The six species assigned to this subfauna are the Gray-cheeked Thrush (which extends south in the east to the Catskill Mountains of central New York); the Water Pipit and the Northern Shrike (both of which are only New World races of holarctic species, and with rather different ranges); the Harris's Sparrow and Smith's Longspur, (both very local and by no means extending across the continent); and the White-crowned Sparrow (which in the west extends far south and has a lowland race along the coast of California). To varying degrees similar difficulties beset such faunal studies in other areas as well.

The problems of untangling faunal and ecological aspects of distribution are further considered in the following chapter.

Value of Faunal Analysis

About one hundred years ago explorers such as Alfred Russel Wallace were sending new species of birds and mammals to Europe from all quarters of the globe. At the same time Wallace and Darwin published their concept of evolution by natural selection, soon to be greatly expanded and extended by Darwin. The setting up of the biogeographic regions was the result of trying to generalize about the distribution of all these species as viewed in the light of evolution. As classification became more refined, and knowledge of distribution more complete, such studies could be carried on with increased assurance. Nevertheless the picture will always remain far from complete.

For a thorough avifaunal analysis of the Hawaiian Islands, for example, we would like to know first what birds arc there and what their distributions are in the islands. Secondly, when and whence they arrived and how much they have changed since reaching Hawaii. In other words, we would like to have the history of the avifauna, past and present. Clearly it will never be possible to achieve such a complete picture of the bird life even of a relatively simple insular situation like the Hawaiian Islands, much less of entire continents. Nevertheless, the main outlines can now be sketched, even on a world-wide basis. Viewed historically, they permit us to understand present patterns of distribution of birds as the contemporary though not final page in the long history of evolution.

Chapter 8

ECOLOGICAL SYSTEMS
OF CLASSIFYING
DISTRIBUTION

If a species of bird is not found in a particular area it may be for one of two reasons. First, the area may be unsuitable for it. Second, it may never have reached the area. It is often possible, however, to be quite sure that local patterns of distribution are ecological. Woodpeckers are absent from marshes and seafowl from forests, not because they cannot reach them but because they cannot live there. Migratory birds frequently pass over many types of habitat and we may assume they would eventually nest in all of them if they were able to do so.

If the distribution of a bird gradually terminates in the absence of any physical barrier the reason is usually ecological even though it is not readily apparent just what is involved. If one selected twenty-five species characteristic of the Great Plains of North America and plotted their nesting ranges, no two would coincide exactly, nor would any two have exactly the same ecology. As between the Prairie Chicken and Sharp-tailed Grouse, for example, the latter clearly prefers a more northern terrain, perhaps with a greater mixture of brush, though the two do occur together in some places.

Since by ecology we include everything in both the physical and biological environment, it may be merely the presence of a superior competitor that keeps a species out of an area.

In situations where both ecological differences

and physical barriers are involved it is more difficult
to tell which is responsible for the presence or absence of a particular bird. In the last chapter we
noted that several birds found on the adjacent continent are absent in the British Isles. Is this because
they never made it across the Channel or because,
having done so, they could not become established?
Subtle ecological deterrents are probably involved
more often than not. Thus Bermuda has a mere
handful of resident songbirds as compared with
North America. Yet many other species occur there
regularly on migration and still others from time to
time. On the other hand, where truly vast distances
are involved, physical barriers may be the determinant. The success with which many introduced
European birds became established in New Zealand
and elsewhere is evidence enough.

In the last chapter we discussed the analysis of
bird distribution on the basis of geographically defined faunas. Such faunas are primarily the result of
historical factors. The history both of the earth—its
changing pattern of islands, mountains, and climates
—and of the birds—their long evolutionary history, so
different in various parts of the globe—is involved.
Ecology cannot be excluded, since if defined broadly
enough, it takes in all these variable and changing
factors. Nevertheless, faunas are the embodiments
of long historical processes.

Ecological systems of classifying bird distribution,
on the other hand, represent an attempt to analyze
and understand distribution in terms of existing hab-

itat. The person interested in such studies has a point of view unlike that of one concerned with faunistics. This can lead to misunderstandings and mistakes, not only as regards bird distribution but also, for example, plant distribution. Such difficulties can be partially avoided if attention is limited to an area where physical barriers are of minor importance. This would be more or less true, for example, of North America.

Life Zones

With this preamble, let us proceed to consider methods of analyzing distribution ecologically. Dr. C. Hart Merriam, first chief of the United States Biological Survey, was impressed by the rapid changes in plant and animal life that one encounters in climbing western peaks such as Mt. Shasta, California, or the San Francisco Peaks in Arizona: first, low barren desert; then sagebrush, followed by piñon-juniper, yellow pine, spruce-fir; and finally alpine meadows above the tree line. In other words, there is a series of rather sharply demarked altitudinal life zones. If, on the other hand, one began at the Gulf of Mexico and proceeded north up the center of the continent, he would have to go thousands of miles, all the way to Hudson Bay, to find comparable changes. These latitudinal life zones, though less sharp than those of the mountains, are otherwise rather similar.

Merriam proceeded to divide the continent into

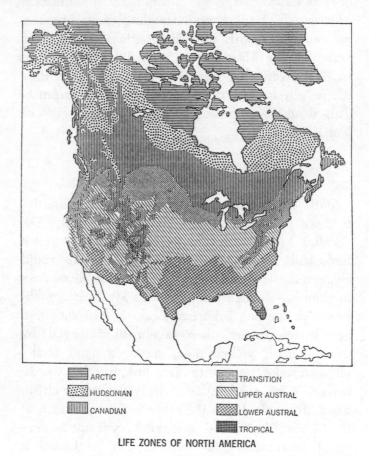

LIFE ZONES OF NORTH AMERICA

Figure 28. C. H. Merriam's life zones of North America.
Modified by C. F. W. Muesebeck and A. D. Cushman.

life zones—Hudsonian Zone, Canadian Zone, and so forth. For each he listed characteristic plants, mammals, birds, and reptiles. The Red-breasted Nuthatch and Ruby-crowned Kinglet, for example, are Canadian Zone birds.

When Merriam sought to explain these life zones he was less successful. They were obviously related to climate. As one climbs a mountain or journeys northward, it becomes colder. Merriam, however, overemphasized temperature and tended to ignore other factors. If, for example, one selects an area in California, in Kansas, and in Virginia, all with similar temperatures, the bird life of the three places will be far from identical! This is largely because of differences in rainfall, or rather in the vegetation which is affected by rainfall. Hence Merriam had to modify his system to include eastern and western zones in the same temperature belt.

Regardless of any shortcomings of interpretation, Merriam's life zones do represent a valid generalization about the distribution of North American plants and animals. Various later systems have sought to improve or refine this system.

Biotic Provinces

Professor Lee R. Dice, for example, divided North America (including Mexico) into twenty-eight "biotic provinces." He defined a biotic province as "a considerable and continuous geographic area characterized by the occurrence of one or more impor-

tant ecologic associations that differ, at least in pro-
portional area covered, from the associations of
adjacent provinces." This definition does a certain
amount of hedging, and tacitly admits that one biotic province may contain a number of associations
some of which occur, though less extensively, in
other provinces. Dice's "ecologic associations," like
Merriam's "life zone indicators," are groups of plants
and animals characteristic of a particular region or
environment. It is doubtful if Dice's system repre-
sents a marked improvement. Some of his provinces
are heterogeneous, for as noted he allows "one or
more" important ecologic associations in a province.

It will be apparent that by recognizing additional

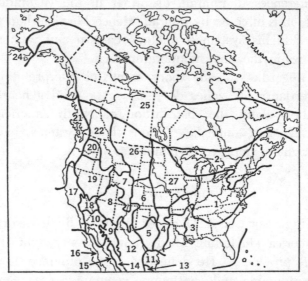

Figure 29. Biotic provinces of North America. After L. R.
Dice.

life zones or biotic provinces one can make them more consistent and homogeneous, yet as their number is multiplied their utility in other respects is diminished. If we eventually have a separate province or zone for each locality they will have lost their value as generalizations.

Biomes

The ecological systems of Merriam and of Dice consider both plants and animals. Some ecologists, however, emphasize the fundamental importance of the vegetation. Plants are more directly responsive to the physical environment—soil, rainfall, temperature—than are animals. Birds, insects, and other animals are, of course, dependent directly or indirectly upon the vegetation. Some birds, such as crossbills which feed only on the seed-cones of evergreen trees, are strictly limited to certain types of vegetation. But birds that feed on insects or, as in the case of birds of prey, upon mammals and birds are often not limited by vegetation. Indeed there are falcons specialized for catching small birds migrating across the Mediterranean and also the Sahara Desert, regions devoid of surface vegetation.

The basic unit of plant ecology is the "biome," defined as the final and definitive, or "climax," vegetation of any particular region. North American examples of biomes are the tundra, the northern coniferous forests, the eastern broad-leafed forests, and the prairie. Each of these does to some extent have

BIOMES OF NORTH AMERICA

TUNDRA   DECIDUOUS FOREST   GRASSLAND   CREOSOTE-BUSH DESERT

SAGEBRUSH

CONIFEROUS FOREST   COASTAL AND INTERIOR CHAPARRAL-PIÑON-JUNIPER

Figure 30. Biomes of North America. After F. A. Pitelka.

its characteristic birds. Although one soon encounters difficulties in trying to classify birds according to such a system, it is still worthwhile to discuss these difficulties since to some extent they apply to all other ecological systems as well.

1. The biomes are not uniform. Thus in the Arctic there is low, wet tundra on which shore birds and waterfowl nest in vast numbers, and higher, barren tundra with very few birds at all.

2. The biomes often vary tremendously from season to season. Even in much of the tropics the vegetation is very different in the wet and dry seasons. Resident birds must, in some species, change their feeding and other habits in winter and summer. Migrants simply move out of the area.

3. If the climax vegetation is destroyed, by man or by natural fires, floods, or climatic changes, it may be centuries before it is restored, if ever. Typically a prolonged "succession" takes place, each stage of which has different birds. For example, if eastern forest is cleared, there follows first grassy fields with birds such as the Vesper Sparrows and Meadowlarks; then brush with Chestnut-sided Warblers and Towhees; then trees such as birches and poplars, and finally, a century later, the climax forest of oak or maple reappears, along with the treetop birds that were there in the original forest. Vast areas of the world have a subclimax vegetation, even where there has been no human influence. The southeastern United States is covered by pine forest which,

it is believed, would go into broad-leafed forest were it not for the fact that the area has been periodically swept by lightning-caused fires. Thus, many biomes contain areas of subclimax vegetation which, so far as birds are concerned, appear like some other biome. Prairie birds nest in open, grassy places in the forest biomes, and so forth. Birds are governed by the general aspect or appearance of vegetation, not by the exact species of plants present or their long-term status in the local flora.

4. Where one biome gives way to another there are often huge stretches of intermediate habitat. The aspen parklands of central Canada are intermediate between the prairie and the northern evergreen forest, and to a degree have the birds of the biome they most resemble, the eastern hardwoods.

5. In mountains there are great local variations in temperature and rainfall and as a result several types of climax vegetation within a small area. Their complexity, when brought down to the level of bird distribution, is so great as to defy generalization or at least to make it less worthwhile.

6. Birds exhibit the so-called "edge effect"—that is, many species prefer the edges of forests or prairies or marshes. If a border of willows and cottonwoods extends along a river through a prairie, this habitat, because of the presence of water and of trees for nesting, will have a richer and denser bird life than the surrounding prairies. Hence the distribution of birds frequently does not agree very well with the prevailing vegetation. It is well known that only a

small number of birds prefer the interior of an un-
broken habitat such as spruce-fir woods and almost
none are dependent upon a single plant in the way
that numerous insects are. Many species such as the
Red-tailed Hawk, Robin, and Great Horned Owl are
found in a truly impressive variety of habitats.

7. It is impossible to rule out historical factors al-
together. Even in such a relatively continuous and
uniform biome as the North American tundra, the
birds are not identical in the eastern and western
parts of the continent. Is this because of subtle distinctions in the present habitats or because of events
during the Ice Ages which affected the species concerned? Probably it is the latter. Farther south on
the continent the presence of many pairs of eastern
and western species such as the Blue Jay and the
Steller's Jay indicates long separation by the intervening plains. This separation may have been even
more complete during the Glacial Age.

8. The winter, migratory, and breeding habitats
of migrant birds are often very different.

9. The biomes themselves have changed during
geological time as the climate altered or as new
groups of plants evolved.

If birds are classified in accordance with vegetation at a lower level than the biome, some of the
above difficulties may be avoided but others are encountered. A botanist may recognize a dozen different plant associations in an eastern fresh-water
marsh yet few, if any, of these will have species of

birds restricted to them. Almost every species of marsh bird will have at least slightly different preferences. Some of the most characteristic ones, such as the Red-winged Blackbird, often occur, sometimes even when nesting, away from marshes.

A classification of land birds based upon vegetation types is nevertheless perhaps the most satisfactory ecological one available. If a forest burns the forest birds go with it and are replaced by larks or sparrows. The habitat so far as birds are concerned must be evaluated in terms of what it is, not of what it was in the past or may be in the future.

The ecological factors responsible for the distribution of sea birds are of considerable interest. That arctic and antarctic waters have different species from the tropics has always been apparent.

In 1936, The American Museum published *Oceanic Birds of South America* by R. C. Murphy. The author, the leading authority on marine birds, demonstrated that the ocean is divided into biotic realms, some of which are as sharply separated as land from sea or mountain from plain. In certain areas, because of ocean currents, the configuration of the ocean bottom, or other reasons, there are rather sudden changes in water temperature and in its oxidation. These result in very different concentrations and kinds of plankton and marine life, which in turn affect the birds. The cool Humboldt, or Peruvian, Current which sweeps up the west coast of South America and then out toward the Galápagos Islands is an example. Highly oxygenated, teeming with plankton, these waters support the largest colonies of birds in the world, those of the Peruvian Guano islands. As noted elsewhere, even penguins have followed these cool waters northward.

A relatively few miles north and west of the Humboldt Current one enters calm tropical waters. Here birds are much less numerous and the species are widespread pan-tropical ones.

The distribution of marine birds is also of particular interest as an example of the difficulty of disentangling ecological and historical factors. The vast expanses of open water would seem to present a marine bird with an open avenue for range expansion, subject only to its ecological needs. Yet the separation of the two regions of cold polar waters by the tropics means that evolution has proceeded more or less independently in the far north and the far south. A few birds such as the Gannet and the Skua have crossed this barrier. Others, such as the auks, have never done so. Their absence in the far south cannot, therefore, be considered an indication that the area is not suited to their requirements; indeed one would expect them to thrive there.

We have considered ecological classifications of birds against a faunal background—North America or the Nearctic Region. Ecologists, however, are not interested in geographic limitations. Some of the biomes such as desert, grassland, and tundra are more or less world-wide. There are also other world-wide, ecological associations such as fresh-water marshes. Botanists will doubtless disagree as to the extent to which biomes can be recognized on a global basis. Coniferous forests are more or less similar wherever they occur. Yet there is a vast difference between lowland pine forest in Nicaragua and coniferous forest in Alaska. Deserts are found on all continents, but their vegetation is often very distinct not merely as regards the species or families of plants represented (the cacti, for example, are New World), but also as to general aspect or appearance. Nevertheless birds are so widespread that one sometimes finds closely related or even the same species occupying similar habitats almost throughout the world. Thus some of the ibises and herons are world-wide, and swallows and swifts much the same from continent to continent.

The isolation responsible for faunal differences has caused evolution to proceed more or less independently in many parts of the globe. Yet there is a tendency for the main ecological niches to be filled. Everywhere one finds marsh birds and forest birds, insect eaters and seed eaters, ground dwellers and treetop dwellers. At the same time evolution is highly opportunistic, and one finds many unique and specialized birds restricted in range and without close counterparts elsewhere. Samuel Butler could not understand why South America and only South America should have toucans with brilliant beaks a foot long. Sometimes we stress the basic similarities of all birds (or all living things), sometimes their infinite variety. This variety is inevitable and to be expected in a world where various regions, such as South America, have been isolated and have followed their own unique, evolutionary pathways for literally tens of millions of years.

The moral is that although the rain forests of Brazil and Borneo look the same, this similarity is valid only up to a point. Most of the many thousands of species of plants and animals making up these two forest communities are not the same. Even the few that are the same are not identical ecologically.

The same would be true of other comparisons, such as the deserts of Australia and Arizona. So great is the profligacy, so endless the potential of evolution, that even recent volcanic islands perhaps no more than a million years old, such as the Galápagos, have given rise to many unique types. Thus one finds there a finch that uses a twig to poke grubs from crevices; another that hops about on iguanas in search of ticks.

Purely ecological grouping of birds, regardless of area and species, into such categories as marsh birds, desert birds, and so forth is nevertheless of value, especially to the physiologist or to the functional anatomist, who is interested in how various species or groups have responded to such environmental stresses as heat and aridity. It might also be of interest to compare the number of species found in, let us say, 10,000 square miles of tropical rain forest with the number found in an equal area of desert. But ecological classifications on a world-wide basis, though of value for such special studies, cannot be precise enough to be of much general utility.

Today's student of distribution, whether ecologist or not, will not be inclined to spend further time wrestling with such concepts as life zones, biotic provinces and faunas. These concepts are based upon such variable data—the ranges of species—that they lack precision. Instead, he may study a single local community in depth in an attempt to understand, so far as possible, how the species interact, and what controls their numbers. Such studies might be restricted to a single species of bird, to all the birds in the area, or to the entire biotic community. In any case, each species will affect the community and be affected by it.

Such a study will tend to be pinpointed in time and space. The community will not be exactly the same fifty miles away, nor was it the same fifty years ago. In a sense no sparrow falls to the ground without its effect, however small, on the biological cosmos.

Thus we are no longer so greatly interested in the total range of a bird—which is rather easily determined anyway. Rather, we wish to understand how it maintains itself and in what numbers and situations in a dynamic and complex ecological world. To the extent that we can elucidate this microdistribution, we shall be able to understand what is controlling the total range of the species.

FURTHER READING

Clements, Frederick E., and Shelford, Victor E. *Bio-ecology*. Wiley (1939).

Darlington, P. J. *Zoogeography*. Wiley (1957).

Darwin, Charles. *The Voyage of the Beagle*.
The Origin of Species. London, Murray (1859 and later editions).

Dice, Lee R. *Biotic Provinces of North America*. University of Michigan Press (1943).

Dorst, Jean. *The Migration of Birds*. Houghton Mifflin (1962).

Griffin, Donald R. *Bird Migration*. Natural History Press (1964).

Grinnell, Joseph. "The Designation of Birds' Ranges." *Auk*, 44:322–324 (1927).

Kendeigh, S. Charles. "History and Evolution of Various Concepts of Plant and Animal Communities in North America." *Ecology*, 35:152–171 (1954).

Klopfer, Peter. "Behavioral Aspects of Habitat Selection: The Role of Early Experience." *Wilson Bulletin*, 75:15–22 (1963).

Lack, David. "The Psychological Factor in Bird Distribution." *British Birds*, 71:130–136 (1937).

Lanyon, Wesley E. *Biology of Birds*, Natural History Press (1963).

Mayr, Ernst. "History of the North American Bird Fauna." *Wilson Bulletin*, 58:3–41 (1946).

Merriam, C. Hart. "Results of a Biological Survey of the San Francisco Mountain Region and Desert of the

Little Colorado, Arizona." *North American Fauna*, No. 3 (1890).

Murphy, Robert Cushman. *Oceanic Birds of South America*. American Museum of Natural History (1936).

Peterson, Roger T. "Life Zones, Biomes, or Life Forms?" *Audubon Magazine*, 44:21–30 (1932).

Pitelka, Frank A. "Distribution of Birds in Relation to Major Biotic Communities." *American Midland Naturalist*, 25:113–137 (1941).

Shelford, Victor E. (Editor). "Bird Distribution and Ecological Concepts: A Symposium." *Wilson Bulletin*, 51:191–201, 243–252 (1945).

Van Tyne, Josselyn, and Berger, Andrew J. *Fundamentals of Ornithology*, Chap. 6. Wiley (1959).

Wallace, Alfred Russel. *Geographical Distribution of Animals*. Two vols., Harper (1876).

Welty, Joel Carl. *The Life of Birds*, Chap. 20. Knopf (1963).

INDEX

Accipters, 115
Africa, 12, 21, 23, 35, 43, 47, 59, 102, 119, 128 (*see also* specific regions); broadbills in, 119; Ciconiiformes in, 113; *Corvus* in, 123; elephants in, 84–85; endemic groups, 131, 132, 133, 134; flamingos in, 113; Galliformes in, 115; magpies in, 122; and migration, 52–53; owls in, 115; Psittaciformes in, 116; ratites in, 109, 110; Secretary-bird in, 114
Age of Reptiles, 68
Alaska, 10, 11, 12, 32, 97, 158; magpies in, 122; and migration, 54
Alaskan-Siberian land bridges, 11, 12, 29, 116
Albatrosses, 42–43, 47, 110; Laysan, 47; predators and, 65; Wandering, 47
Aleutian Islands, 57, 111
Alice Springs, Australia, 42
Allen, Robert Porter, 94
Amazonia, 21, 54, 69
Amazon River, 22
American Chestnut (tree), 67
American Crows, 55
American Merganser, 79
American Museum of Natural History, 5, 52, 137, 156
American Red-tailed Hawk, 84
American Robin, 45, 100–1
American vultures, 116
Anatidae, 79
Andes and Andean species, 35, 116, 117
Anhimidae, 79
Anseriformes, 79, 112
Antarctic, Antarctica, 3, 101; Sphenisciformes of, 110
Ant-birds, 130
Apes, 92
Apodiformes, 117
Aransas River, 94

Archaeopteryx, 14, 77, 134
Arctic, 3, 36, 110, 138, 140; biomes, 153; Charadriiformes in, 111; and migration, 49–55
Argentina, 22, 131
Arizona, 147, 159
Asia, 12, 35, 95, 96, 119, 128 (*see also* Far East; Orient; specific areas); broadbills in, 119; endemic regional groups, 129, 131, 132; flamingos in, 113; Horned Lark, 133; ratites in, 109
Asiatic blight, 67
Atlantic, North, 53
Audubon Society, 94
Auks, 112, 132, 157
Australia and Australian species, 15, 22, 42, 67, 129, 130, 133 (*see also* Australian Region); Anseriformes in, 112; Black Swan, 35; Cattle Egret in, 102; *Corvus* in, 123; endemic groups, 137, 138, 139, 159; flamingo fossils in, 113; Galliformes in, 115; honey eaters, 120; Lyrebirds restricted to, 119, 134; owls in, 116; plains wanderers in, 114; Psittaciformes in, 116; ratites in, 109, 110; scrub wrens in, 119; songbirds in, 119, 120 (*see also* specific birds)
Australian Region, 129, 131, 133, 134
Aves, 79
Avocets, 112
Azure-winged Magpie, 122

Babblers, 35, 120
Bahama Islands, 4, 96
Baja California, 83
Baltimore orioles, 54, 72
Barn Owl, 115
Barred Owl, Eastern, 84
Barriers, physical, 21–36, 81, 117, 130–31, 145, 146
Bavaria, 14, 134

Beagle, H.M.S., 4
Bears, Polar, 3
Beebe, William, 115
Bee eaters, 133
Bell magpies, 129
Belted Kingfisher, 29–32; nesting of, 45
Beneficial factors, 71–73, 98. *See also* Climate; Food; Man
Bering Strait, 22
Bermuda, 146
Biogeographic regions, 127–42
Biomes, 151–60
"Biotic provinces," 149–51
Birds of Paradise, 120, 129
Bitterns, sun, 114
Blackbirds, 34, 48, 128; Redwinged, 156; Yellow-headed, 57–58
Black-headed Grosbeaks, 72
Black Swan, Australian, 35
Blight, Asiatic, 67
Bluebirds, 101; Eastern, 70; Fairy, 129
Blue Jays, 41, 100, 155
Boat-billed Herons, 113
Bobolinks, 61
Bobwhites, 32, 77; shelter for, 43, 45
Boobies, 111, 130
Borneo, 138, 159
Bowerbirds, 120, 129
Brazil, 3, 159
Bridges, land, 11–12, 22–23, 29, 116
Bristle-thighed Curlew, 96–97
British Columbia, 56, 59, 83, 101
British Isles, 10, 22, 29, 95, 138, 146; fishing fleet, 73; "Mag" Pie in England, 122; stragglers in, 25
Broadbills, 119, 133
Budgies. *See* Parakeets
Bulbuls, 120
Bullfinch, 54
Bullock's orioles, 72
Buntings, 72, 121
Bustards, 114, 133
Buteos, 115
Butler, Samuel, 158
Button quail, 114
Buzzards, Eurasian Common, 84

Caged birds, 57; canaries, 71
California, 40, 66, 92, 95, 107, 140, 147; Baja, 83; Gulf of, 112; magpies in, 122
California Condors, 83, 92, 93, 97, 116
California House Finch, 34
Canada, 45, 53, 57, 69, 83 (*see also* specific regions); biomes in, 154; Cattle Egret in, 102; Whooping Cranes in, 94, 95
Canadian Zone, 149
Canaries, 71
Canvasback Ducks, 59, 77–78
Canvasback on a Prairie Marsh, The, 59
Cape Barren Goose, 15, 112
Cape Horn, 111
Cape Sable Island, Nova Scotia, 70, 139
Capistrano, 46–47
Caracaras, 84
Carbon 14 tests, 68
Cardinals, 32, 35, 71–72
Cariamas, 114, 130
Carolina Parakeet, 116
Carolina Wren, 32
Caroline Islands, 26, 27
Cassowaries, 109, 129
Categories, 107–23. *See also* Families; Orders; Species
Cathartidae, 107–8. *See also* Vultures
Catskill Mountains, 140
Cattle Egret, 101–2
Celebes, 115, 138
Central America, 53, 128
Ceylon, 129
Chance, and distribution, 25–33, 81
Chapin, James P., 52
Charadriiformes, 111–12
Chemicals, 71–73; DDT, 100–1
Chestnut, American, 67
Chestnut-sided Warblers, 153
Chickadees, 48, 69
Chile, 51
China, 121, 134
Chipping Sparrows, 60
Chukar Partridge, 33
Ciconiiformes, 113
Clamatores, 119–20
"Classes," 79–80
Classification, 78–80, 141 (*see also* Categories); ecological, 143–60
Cliff Swallows, 46–47

Climate, 10–11 ff, 49–55, 67–70, 87, 137, 149. *See also* Temperature; specific regions
Climax vegetation, 151 ff
Cold. *See* Temperature; Winter; specific areas
Colombia, 133
Common Buzzard, Eurasian, 84
Common Caracara, 84
Communication between populations, 82
Competition, 89–92, 101. *See also* specific regions, species
Condors, California, 83, 92, 93, 97, 116
Congo, 3, 52
Congo Peacock, 115
Continents, 131, 138, 139. *See also* specific continents
Cook, Capt. James, 97
Cooper's Hawk, 89
Cormorants, 111, 130
Corvidae, 121–23, 133. *See also* Crows
Corvus, 122–23. *See also* Crows
"Cospecific" species, 85
Cossypha Thrush, 59
Cotingas, 130
Cover (and shelter), 43–49
Cowbirds, 60–61, 99, 100
Crab Plovers, 112, 133
Cranes, 51, 114; Sandhill, 58; Whooping, 93–95, 96, 97
Cretaceous period, 13, 68, 135
Crossbills, 54, 151
Crows, 39, 45, 57, 107, 120, 121–23, 133; as predators, 65; and roosting, 48, 55; wattled, 129
Cuckoos, 51
Curassows, 115
Curlews, Bristle-thighed, 96–97
Cyanocorax Jays, 121

Dams, 72
Darlington, P. J., 134, 137
Darwin, Charles, 4–5, 77, 78, 90, 141
Darwin's Finches, 4–5
Dating of fossils, 68, 85
DDT, 100–1
Declining species, 92–100
Deserts and desert birds, 41–42, 46, 56, 151, 157, 158, 159. *See also* specific birds

Diatryma, 135, 136
Dice, Lee R., 149–51
Disease, 67, 98
Dodos, 3, 16, 29, 66, 128
Dominant species, 100–3
Doves, 25, 41–42; Turtle, 101
Downy Woodpecker, 59, 90
Drongos, 120, 133
Ducks, 22, 45, 51, 61, 112, 140; Canvasbacks, 59, 77–78; Eider, 48–49; Mallard, 61, 78–79, 85; Musk, 112; Pink-eared, 112; Pintail, 78–79, 85; Wood, 77–78

Eagles, 40; Golden, 83
Earthworms, 101
East Africa, 35, 59
Eastern Barred Owl, 84
Eastern Bluebird, 70
Eastern meadowlarks, 87
East Indies, 119, 129
"Ecological niche," 55–62
Ecological requirements, 35–62. *See also* specific areas, environments, groups, requirements
Ecological systems, 145–60
"Edge effect," 154
Egg-laying: food and, 40; shelter and, 43, 45
Egrets: Cattle, 101–2; Great, 113
Egypt, 41
Eider Ducks, 48–49
Elephant-birds, 71, 109
Elephants, 84–85
Elm trees, 100
Emperor Penguin, 69
Emus, 109, 129
Enemies, 56, 65–67. *See also* Man; Predators
England. *See* British Isles
English Channel, 22
Eocene period, 12, 13, 135, 136
Errington, Paul L., 43
Ethiopian Region, 128, 132, 133, 134
Eurasia, 29, 111, 122; endemic regional groups, 128, 131, 132
Eurasian Common Buzzard, 84
Europe, 10, 22, 33, 67, 101, 141 (*see also* Old World; specific countries); flamingos in, 113; migration in, 49; Strigiformes in, 115
European Goldfinches, 33

Everglade Kites, 39
Everglades, Florida, 116
Evolution, 4–5, 9–16, 72, 77 ff, 118, 141–42, 157 ff (*see also* Patterns of distribution; specific groups, regions, species, etc.); and ecological niche, 60; the regions and past distribution, 134–37

Fair Isle, 25
Fairy bluebirds, 129
Falconiformes, 115–16
Falcons, 151; Peregrine, 45, 115
Falkland Islands, 131
Families, 79–80, 107 ff, 127 ff
Far East, 122, 132. *See also* Asia; specific countries
Farm ponds, 72
Fauna, geographical patterns of distribution of, 127–42, 146
Feather mites, 66
Feeders, bird, 72
Fieldfares, 26
Fiji Islands, 116
Finch-billed honey creepers, 91
Finches, 34, 41–42, 121, 128, 159; Bullfinch, 54; California House, 34; Darwin's, 4–5, 90; European Goldfinch, 33; Weaver, 35
Fish hawks, 115
Fishing fleet, British, 73
Flamingos, 35, 113; nesting, 47; water for, 43
Flies, bloodsucking, 67
Flightless birds, 65, 70–71 (*see also* specific birds); giant, 109–10
Flock pigeons, 42
Flocks, 25
Florida, 22, 70, 102, 112, 129, 136; Carolina Parakeets in, 116; Everglades, 116; flamingos in, 113; Keys, 98
Flowerpecker, 120
Flycatchers, 46, 51, 69, 89, 120; tyrant, 131
Food, 39–41, 56, 100 (*see also* specific environments, species); and migration, 51 ff; suburban bird feeders, 72
Forests, 145–60 *passim* (*see also* Rain forests); vertical distribution of niches in, 61–62
Formosa, 54

Fossils, 11–12, 14, 15, 77, 78, 83, 114, 134–37; Anseriformes, 112; dating of, 68, 85; flamingo, 113; vulture, 107–8
Fresh-water groups, 113. *See also* specific areas, groups
Frigate-birds, 47–48, 111, 130
Frogs, meadow, 83
Fulmar Petrels, 73, 110

Galápagos Islands, 4, 9, 90, 110, 138, 156; tortoises, 29
Galeated (Nuku Hiva) Pigeon, 24, 25
Galliformes, 114–15
Gallinules, Purple, 31, 32–33
Game birds, 59–60. *See also* specific birds
Gannets, 111, 157
Gause (ecologist), 89
Gaviiformes, 111
Geese, 15, 16, 112; Cape Barren, 15, 115; and migration, 51, 112
"Genus," genera, 78 ff, 107, 121–23, 127 ff. *See also* specific genera
Geography. *See* Patterns of distribution; Physical barriers; specific environments, regions
Geological timetable, 13–14
Germany, 41. *See also* Bavaria
Giant flightless birds, 109–10
Giller, D. R., 87
Glaciation, 10, 12, 68. *See also* Ice Age
Glossy Ibis, 22, 113
Golden Eagle, 83
Golden-fronted Woodpecker, 87, 89
Goldfinches, European, 33
Gray-cheeked Thrush, 140
Great Auk, 112
Great Britain. *See* British Isles
Great Egret, 113
Great Horned Owl, 83, 155
Great Plains, 93, 145
Grebes, sun, 114
Greenland, 10, 26, 48
Grosbeaks: Black-headed, 72; Rose-breasted, 54, 72
Grouse, 114, 132; Plains (Prairie Chicken), 128, 145; Red, 138; Ruffed, 59–60, 77; Sand, 32; Sharp-tailed, 145

Gruiformes, 114
Guadalupe Island Caracara, 84
Guano Islands, 157
Gulf of California, 112
Gulf Coast, 93
Gulf of Mexico, 147
Gulls, 45, 73, 112; roosting, 48

Hairy Woodpecker, 59, 90
Haiti, 54
Hammerhead Storks, 113, 128
Harmful factors, 65–67, 98. *See also* Predators
Harris's Sparrow, 140
Hawaii, island of, 91, 129
Hawaiian Goose, 16
Hawaiian Islands, 15–16, 23, 26 ff, 35, 90, 92, 129; Anseriformes in, 112; *Corvus* in, 123; disease in, 67, 98; endemic groups, 138, 141; honey creepers in, 90–91, 129; volcanoes, 9
Hawks, 115–16, 140; Cooper's, 89; fish, 115; North American Marsh, 84; as predators, 65, 66–67, 118; Red-tailed, 40, 66–67, 84, 155
Heat. *See* Temperature
Hedge sparrows, 128
Helmet shrikes, 121, 129
Heredity, 60, 97. *See also* Evolution; Species and speciation
Hermit Thrush, 81
Herons, 102, 113, 158
Herperonis, 135
Himalayas, 8, 17, 128, 132
Historical factors. *See* Evolution
Hoatzins, 115, 130
Holarctic Region, 132, 140
Honey creepers, 120–21, 129; finch-billed, 91
Honey eaters, Australian, 120, 129
Honey guides, 133
Hooded Merganser, 79
Horizontal vs. vertical distribution, 61–62
Hornbills, 129, 132, 133
Horned Lark, 133
Horned Owl, Great, 83, 155
Horse family, 11–12
Horvath, Otto, 101
House Finch, California, 34
House Sparrows, 33, 101
Hudson Bay, 147

Hudsonian Zone, 149
Humboldt Current, 156–57
Hummingbirds, 3–4, 117; eating habits, 40, 41; Ruby-throated, 77–78
Hungarian Partridge, 33
Hungary, 22
Huxley, Sir Julian, 5
Huxley, T. H., 5

Ibises, 113, 158; Glossy, 22, 113
Ice Age (Glacial Age), 23, 53–54, 68, 93, 108, 112, 116, 155. *See also* Glaciation
Ichthyornis, 136
Incubator-birds (megapodes), 115, 129
India, 35, 113, 115, 122, 129, 132; Psittaciformes in, 116
Indian elephants, 84–85
Indian Ocean area, 112
Indian Region, 129. *See also* India
Indigo buntings, 72
Interbreeding. *See* Species and speciation; specific groups, regions, etc.
Introduced species, 33–36
Iowa, 93
Ipswich Sparrow, 86, 139
Irrigation, 72
Islands, 8, 9, 10, 23 ff, 47, 65–66, 97–99, 115, 137–39 (*see also* specific islands, locations); and speciation, 84 ff
"Isolating mechanisms," 82
Isolation, geographical, 72, 80–92 ff, 103. *See also* Islands; specific areas, birds
Isthmuses, 22
Ivory-billed Woodpeckers, 57

Jacamars, 130
Jack-pine Warbler. *See* Kirtland's Warbler
Jaegers, 43, 51, 130
Japan, 132; magpies in, 122
Japanese White-eye, 99
Jays, 121–22; Blue, 41, 100, 155; *Cyanocorox*, 121; ground-living, 122; *Perisoreus*, 121; *Platylophus*, 121; *Platysmurus*, 121; *Pseudopodoces*, 122; Steller's, 155
Jurassic Era, 13, 14, 134

Kagus, 114, 129, 138
Kansas, 135
Kea parrot, 116
Kestrels, 55, 115
Kingfishers, Belted, 29–32, 45
Kinglets, 54; Ruby-crowned, 149
King Vulture, 69
Kirtland's Warbler, 4, 96, 98–99
Kite, Everglade, 39
Kivu Mountains, 119
Kiwis, 65, 109, 129
Knot, 111

Lake Magadi, 47
Land barriers, 21–36. See also Physical barriers
Land birds, 8, 22, 23–36, 130, 138, 156. See also specific groups, species
Land bridges, 11–12, 22–23, 29, 116
Language, 82
Larks, 133, 156; Horned, 133; meadowlarks, 87, 101; Skylarks, 34–35
Laysan Albatrosses, 47
Lazuli buntings, 72
Lesser Sunda Islands, 131
Life zones, 147–50
Linnaeus, 78
Long Island, 33–34, 81
Longspur, Smith's, 140
Loons, 111, 132
Lorenz, Konrad, 123
Louisiana, 93
Lower Souris River Waterfowl Refuge, 95
Luzon, 54
Lyell, Charles, 4
Lyrebirds, 119, 129, 134

Mackenzie, Canada, 94
Madagascar, 23, 28, 71, 109, 128; Corvus in, 123; endemic groups, 128–29, 132, 137; mesites in, 114; Philepittas in, 119
Magpies, 95–96, 122, 129
Maine, 112
Malaria, 67, 99
Mallards, 61, 78–79, 85
Mammals, 132 (see also specific mammals); climate changes and, 68–69
Mamo, 99

Man, 70–73, 99; species introduced by, 33–36
Manakins, 130
Manchuria, 132
Marine birds (sea birds), 8, 47–49, 130, 156–57 (see also specific birds); civilization and, 73; and water requirements, 42–43
Marine Region, 130
Marquesas, 25
Marsh birds, 113, 114, 155–56, 157, 159 (see also specific birds); shelter for, 43
Marsh Hawk, North American, 84
Massapequa, L.I., 33
Matthew, W. D., 137
Mauritius, 3, 16, 128
Mayr, Ernst, 5
Meadow frogs, 83
Meadowlarks, 87, 101, 153
Mediterranean Sea, 151
Megapodes (incubator-birds), 115, 129
Meinertzhagen, Richard, 92
Mergansers, 79
Merriam, C. Hart, 147–49, 151
Mesites, 114
Mexico, 83, 122; endemic groups, 128, 129, 131, 149; Gulf of, 147
Michigan, 4, 96
"Micro-distribution," 81, 89
Micronesian Pigeon, 25
Middle East, 101, 132
Midway Island, 47
Midwest, United States, 87, 101. See also specific areas
Migrants and migration, 25 ff, 49–55, 57, 138, 145, 155 (see also specific birds); and declining species, 96–97; night, 25, 61
Miocene period, 13
Mites, feather, 66
Moas, 71, 109
Moluccas (Spice Islands), 129, 131
Montana, 136
Mosquitoes, 67, 99
Motmots, 130
Mountains, 8, 9, 12, 147, 154
Mount Shasta, 147
Mousebirds, 128, 129
Murphy, R. C., 156
Musk Duck, 112

Mutations, 97
Mynahs, 35
Myxomatosis, 67

National Audubon Society, 94
Nearctic Region, 128, 131–32, 135, 140, 155, 157
Nebraska, 94
Neocathartes, 136
Neotropical Region, 129–30, 131, 132
Nesting, 40, 43 ff, 53, 55, 73, 100 (see also specific birds); and declining species, 94 ff
New Caledonia, 114, 129, 138
New England, 57, 83. See also specific places
New Guinea, 21, 109, 120, 129; Corvus in, 123
New Jersey, 34, 102
New World, 16, 107–8, 133, 136 (see also North America; etc.); Apodiformes in, 117; parrots, 117; songbirds, 119–21; vultures, 136
New York, 33, 101. See also specific areas
New Zealand, 15, 23, 25, 28, 34–35, 132, 137, 138, 146; Anseriformes in, 112; Kea parrot in, 116; kiwis in, 65, 129; migration to, 51; moas in, 70–71, 109; ratites in, 109, 110; wattled crows in, 129; wrens, 119, 129
Nicaragua, 158
Nightingales, 41
Nightjar, Pennant-winged, 52–53
Night migrants, 25, 61
North, Far (see also specific regions): roosting sites, 48–49
North Africa, 128
North America, 10, 11, 12, 25, 29, 33, 93–96 (see also New World; specific birds, regions); absence of ratites in, 109; biomes, 151–60; "biotic provinces," 149–51; Charadriiformes in, 111, 112; climate and distribution in, 68–69; endemic regional groups, 128–37 passim; evolution in, 77–78, 86, 93–96, 102, 135–37; Gaviiformes in, 111; life zones, 147–50; migration, 49; song-

birds, 120–21, 146 (see also specific birds)
North American Marsh Hawk, 84
North Atlantic, 53
Northern birds, 48, 53–54. See also specific birds, regions
Northern Shrike, 140
Nova Scotia: Cape Sable Island, 70, 139; Sable Island, 86
Nuku Hiva Pigeon, 24, 25
Nutcrackers, 122
Nuthatches, 51; Red-breasted, 149

Oceania, 27, 129. See also specific island groups
Oceanic Birds of South America, 156
Oceans. See Marine birds; Water; specific oceans
Old World, 12, 16, 22, 95, 101–2, 107–8 (see also Europe; specific regions); endemic regional groups, 133, 135; jays, 121, 122; parrots, 117; songbirds, 119–20 (see also specific birds)
Oligocene period, 13
Orders, 12, 79–80, 107–23
Orient, 114. See also Asia; specific regions
Oriental Region: endemic groups, 129, 131–33, 134; jays in, 121, 122
Origin of Species, 78, 90
Orioles: Baltimore, 54, 72; Bullock's, 72; New World, 120; Old World, 120
Osborn, Henry Fairfield, 68
Oscines, 118, 119–20
Osteodontornis, 136
Ostriches, 109, 110, 128, 129, 134. See also Rheas
Ovenbirds, 60, 130
Owls, 115–16; Barn, 115; Eastern Barred, 84; Great Horned, 83, 155; nesting, 45, 46; as predators, 65, 118; Screech, 45; Short-eared, 26, 27; Snowy, 3, 51, 69, 83; Western Spotted, 84
Oyster-catchers, 112

Pacific Coast (see also specific areas): Wren Tit of, 128
Pacific islands, 97, 115. See also Oceania; specific islands

Pacific Pigeon, 23–25
Palau Islands, 115
Palearctic Region, 128, 131–32, 133, 134
Paleocene period, 13
Panama, Isthmus of, 22
Parakeets, 42, 116
Parasites, 56, 58, 61, 65–67, 99–100
Parrots, 41–42, 116–17; Kea, 116; roosting of, 48
Partridges, 33
Passeriformes, 118–21
Past distribution, 134–37, 141–42. *See also* specific groups, species
Patagonia, 131
Patterns of distribution, geographical, 127–42
Peacock, Congo, 115
Pelecaniformes, 111
Pelicans, 108, 111
Penguins, 36, 110, 130, 134, 157; Emperor, 69; nesting of, 47
Pennant-winged Nightjar, 52–53
Perching birds, 117–21, 140
Peregrine Falcon, 45, 115
Perisoreus Jays, 121
Peruvian Current, 156–57
Peruvian Guano Islands, 157
Pesticides, 71; DDT, 100–1
Petrels, 47, 53, 110–11, 130; Fulmar, 73, 110; predators and, 65; storm, 110–11
Phalaropes, 43, 130, 132; Red, 54–55
Pheasants, 33, 114–15, 129
Philepittas, 120, 128
Philippine Islands, 115, 129
Phoenicopteriformes, 113
Phorhorhacids, 114, 136
Physical barriers, 21–36, 81, 117, 130–31, 145, 146
Pigeons, 23–25, 42, 98
Pine Barrens, Long Island, 81
Pine Warblers, 61
Pink-eared Duck, 112
Pintail ducks, 78–79, 85
Pipit, Water, 140
Pittas, 119, 133
Plains Grouse (Prairie Chicken), 128, 145
Plains wanderers, 114, 129
Plant birds, 130
Plants, biomes and, 151–60
Platte River, 94

Platylophus Jays, 121
Platysmurus Jays, 121
Pleistocene period, 12, 13, 68, 71, 83, 109, 134, 136; Condors in, 116; post-, 113
Pliocene period, 13
Plovers, crab, 112, 133
Polar bears, 3
Polar regions, 6–7, 8 (*see also* specific areas); and migration, 49, 50 ff
Polynesian Islands, 26
Ponape Island, 26, 27
Ponds, farm, 72
Prairie Chicken, 128, 145
Predators, 56, 65–67, 98 ff, 115–16, 151
Procellariiformes, 110–11
Pseudopodoces Jays, 122
Psittaciformes, 116–17
Ptarmigans, 51, 69
Puffbirds, 130
Purple Gallinules, 31, 32–33

Quail, 43, 114. *See also* Bobwhites

Rabbits, 67
Races, 138
Rails, 31, 32–33, 65, 114
Rainfall, 149, 151, 154
Rain forests, 21, 56, 83, 92, 159
Ratites, 109–10
Ravens, 51, 122–23
Reclamation Service, 72
Red-bellied Woodpecker, 87
Red-breasted Nuthatch, 149
Red-eyed Vireo, 62
Red Grouse, 138
Red Phalarope, 54–55
Red-tailed Hawk, 40, 66–67, 155; American, 84
Red-winged Blackbird, 156
Reptiles, Age of, 68
Rheas, 16, 109, 130
Robins, 57, 59, 155; American, 45, 100–1
Rocky Mountains, 122
Rollers, 133
Roosting, 48–49, 55. *See also* specific birds
Rose-breasted Grosbeaks, 54, 72
Rosy Starling, 32
Ruby-crowned Kinglet, 149

Ruby-throated Hummingbird, 77–78
Ruffed Grouse, 59–60, 77
Ryukyu Islands, 122

Sable Island, Nova Scotia, 86
Sage Hen (Prairie Chicken), 128, 145
Sahara Desert, 151
Salt water, 35, 42–43, 47. *See also* Marine birds
Sanderling, 111
San Francisco, 57
San Francisco Peaks, 147
Sand grouse, 32
Sandhill Crane, 58
Sandpipers, 111
Savannah Sparrow, 86
Scarlet Tanagers, 53
Scotland, 111
Screamers, 79, 130
Screech Owl, 45
Scrub-birds, 129
Scrub wrens, Australian, 119
Sea birds. *See* Marine birds
Seaside Sparrow, 70
Seasons, 7, 16, 45, 49–55, 153
Secretary-birds, 114, 128
Selander, R. K., 87
Sharp-tailed Grouse, 145
Shearwater, 110
Sheathbills, 130
Shelter, 43–49
Shoebill storks, 113, 128
Shore birds, 22, 51, 111–12, 113, 140, 146. *See also* specific birds
Short-eared Owl, 26
Shrikes, 65, 120; helmet, 121, 129; Northern, 140; vanga, 129
Siberia, 10, 11, 12, 116, 135
Skuas, 112, 157
Skylarks, 34–35
Smith's Longspur, 140
Snipe, 111
Snowy Owl, 3, 51, 69, 83
Solomon Islands, 22
Song, 82, 118–19
Songbirds, 22 ff, 45, 56–57, 118–23. *See also* Land birds; specific species
Song Sparrow, 56, 57
Sooty Terns, 47
Souris River Waterfowl Refuge, 95
South America, 10, 16, 23, 79, 102, 110 (*see also* specific regions); Ciconiiformes in, 113; Clamatores in, 119; *Corvus* absent in, 123; endemic groups, 129 ff, 156 ff; flamingos, 113; Galliformes in, 115; Gruiformes in, 114; hummingbirds, 117; jays, 121; Psittaciformes, 116–17; ratites, 109; songbirds, 119, 120, 121 (*see also* specific birds)
South American Ostrich. *See* Rheas
South Dakota, 95
Spain, 102, 122
Sparrows, 156; Cape Sable Seaside, 70; Chipping, 60; Harris's, 140; Hedge, 128; House, 33, 101; Ipswich, 86, 139; Savannah, 86; Song, 56, 57; Vesper, 153; White-crowned, 140
Specialization, 91, 92
Species and speciation, 77–103, 138. *See also* specific areas, species
Spheniisciformes, 110
Spice Islands (Moluccas), 129, 131
Spoonbills, 113
Spotted Owl, Western, 84
Spurred Towhee, 108
Starlings, 25, 33–34, 57, 70, 101, 120; eating habits, 41; nesting, roosting, 55; Rosy, 32; Wattled, migration of, 53
Steller's Jay, 155
Storks, 113, 128
Storm petrels, 110–11
Storms, 25–28, 69–70
Strigiformes, 115–16
Subantarctic, 110
Subarctic, 111
"Subarctic tundra-forest," 140
Subfaunas, 140
Subphylum, 79
Subspecies, 84–85, 90, 138, 139
Suburban bird feeders, 72
Sumatra, 138
Summer, 49–55
Sunbirds, 120, 133
Sun bitterns, 114
Sun grebes, 114
"Superspecies," 84–85
Swallows, 22, 158; Cliff, 46–47; food for, 39, 51; migration, 54;

Swallows (cont'd)
nesting of, 46–47; shelter for, 45
Swans, 51, 112; Australian Black, 35
Swifts, 46, 117, 158
Syrinx, 118–19

Tahiti, 97, 116, 129
Tanagers, 121; Scarlet, 53
Tasmania, 129
Temperature, 6–9, 12, 137, 138, 149, 154, 156–57. See also Climate; specific regions
Teratorns, 136
Terns, 112, 130; Sooty, 47
Territory, 40–41
Tertiary period, 117, 118
Texas, 87, 93–94, 95
Thrashers, 120
Thrushes, 34, 100–1, 120; Cossypha, 59; Fieldfares, 26; Gray-cheeked, 140; Hermit, 81; Turdus, 120; Varied, 59, 101
Tibet, 92, 122
Timetable, geological, 13–14
Tinamous, 109, 130
Tit, Wren, 128
Todies, 130
Tortoises, Galápagos, 29
Toucans, 130, 158
Towhees, 108, 153
Triassic period, 13
Tristan da Cunha, 31, 33
Tropic-birds, 111, 130
Tropics and tropical birds, 52–54, 69, 108, 112–17 passim (see also specific areas, birds); endemic regional groups, 129–30, 131, 134, 138
Trumpeters, 130
Turacos, 128, 129
Turdus thrushes, 120
Turkeys, 77, 115, 128
Turkish Turtle Dove, 101
Turtle Dove, Turkish, 101
Tyrant flycatchers, 131

Udvardy, Miklos, 140
United States, 22, 51, 57–58, 68, 153–54 (see also North America; specific regions); Charadriiformes in, 112; Falconiformes in, 115; Gaviiformes in, 111; Strigiformes in, 115

Vanga shrikes, 129
Varied Thrush, 59, 101
Vegetation, biomes and, 151–60
Vertebrata, 79
Vertical distribution of niches, 61–62
Vesper Sparrows, 153
Vireos, 60; Red-eyed, 62
Voice box, 118–19
Volcanic islands, 9
Vultures, 48, 68, 92, 107–8; American, 116; California Condors, 83, 92, 93, 116; King, 69; Neocathartes, 136

Wake Island, 31, 33
Wallace, Alfred Russel, 4, 141
"Wallace's Line," 131
Wanderers, plains, 114, 129
Wandering Albatross, 47
Warblers, 51, 118, 120; Chestnut-sided, 153; Kirtland's, 4, 96, 98–99; Pine, 61; Wood, 120
Water, 8 (see also Marine birds); barriers, 21–33 ff; and islands (see Islands); requirements, 41–43, 72, 73; and roosting, 47–49
Water buffalo, 102
Waterfowl, 45, 112. See also Marsh birds; Marine birds; Shore birds; specific species
Water Pipit, 140
Wattled crows, 129
Wattled Starling, 53
Weather. See Climate; Rainfall; Seasons; Storms
Weaver finches, 35
West Africa, 21
Western meadowlarks, 87
Western Spotted Owl, 84
West Indies, 23, 28, 98, 102, 129; Corvus in, 123; flamingos in, 113; todies, 130
White-crowned Pigeon, 98
White-crowned Sparrow, 140
White-eyes, 22, 35, 99, 120
White-winged Crossbill, 54
Whooping Crane, 93–95, 96, 97
Windbreaks, 72
Winter, 48–49, 49–55, 69, 70. See also Climate; Migrants and migration

Winter Wren, 29
Wisconsin, 57–58
Woodcock, 39, 111
Wood Duck, 77–78
Woodpeckers, 25, 46, 51, 145;
Downy, 59, 90; Golden-fronted,
87, 89; Hairy, 59, 90; Ivory-
billed, 57; Red-bellied, 87, 89
Wood warblers, 120
Wrens, 29, 40, 43, 118, 120; Aus-

tralian scrub, 119; Carolina, 32;
New Zealand, 119, 129; Winter,
29
Wren Tit, 128
Wyoming, 135

Yellow-headed Blackbird, 57–58
Yucatan, 113

Zebras, 12

DEAN AMADON is Chairman of the Department of Ornithology and Lamont Curator of Birds at The American Museum of Natural History. He received his Bachelor of Science degree from Hobart College in Geneva, New York, and, in 1947, his doctorate from Cornell University. A member of the staff of the Museum since 1937, Dr. Amadon is co-author with Dr. Robert Cushman Murphy of *Land Birds of America,* one of seven authors of the three-volume work, *The Animal Kingdom,* and the author of many articles for scientific journals in this country and abroad. He is a member of the Society for the Study of Evolution, president (1965) of the American Ornithologists' Union, and a past president of the Linnean Society of New York.